In many parts of the world Paul Wilson is known as the Guru of Calm. His work in simplifying meditation practices has led to his methods being used throughout Europe, India, China and Australasia. One newspaper estimates that he has taught over a million people to meditate in the past 40 years.

He's also been a businessman, lecturer, syndicated columnist, director of a medical research foundation and author. His books have sold more than ten million copies and have been translated into more than 24 languages.

Paul Wilson now lives in Australia, near the beach, surfing regularly and playing in his blues band.

Also by Paul Wilson

Calm
no matter what

First published 2014 by Pan Macmillan Australia Pty Ltd
1 Market Street, Sydney, New South Wales, Australia, 2000.

Cataloguing-in-Publication entry is available
from the National Library of Australia
http://catalogue.nla.gov.au

Typeset in 11.5/19 pt ITC Legacy Book by Kirby Jones
Internal text design by Debra Billson
Illustrations by Paul Wilson
Internal photograph by Silvae/Shutterstock.com
Printed in China

Papers used by Pan Macmillan Australia Pty Ltd are natural,
recyclable products made from wood grown in sustainable forests.
The manufacturing processes conform to the environmental
regulations of the country of origin.

Paul Wilson

THE GURU OF CALM

Calm
no matter what

The effortless way to

maintain calm and equilibrium,

whatever the circumstances

MACMILLAN
Pan Macmillan Australia

Contents

I n the eighties I wrote Instant Calm, *a handbook of ways to find a bit of peace and calm when the need arose. It was a book of quick-fix solutions. Even though most of these were not based on methods I'd learned and shared in my decades as a meditation teacher and researcher, they served a useful purpose: short-term relief from painful symptoms such as stress or worry.*

Calm: No Matter What *has a much bigger agenda.*

Our focus now is creating an underlying sense of calm that works both in the short term, but also stays with you – no matter what is going on, what you're experiencing, what life throws your way, or even what state of mind you're in. Once you have this underlying sense of calm, two benefits come your way: you experience the up times with greater satisfaction, and when things go wrong you bounce right back. Your workloads, discomforts and dramas won't change, but you will be able to deal with them dynamically and effectively. With peacefulness at your centre rather than tension and anxiety.

Even better, Calm: No Matter What *is about experiencing life more, appreciating it more, enjoying it more. Not just for a few hours, or days, or even for a particular phase of life, but for your whole life.*

Seeking calm

Calm and equilibrium that sticks

Have you ever spent a few weeks in total relaxation? On a peaceful, away-from-it-all holiday, for instance? Or on a meditation retreat where there was nothing else to do but meditate, gaze at your navel, and eat healthy foods?

You come away from it feeling like a new person. Strong, energised, full of ideas, ready to take on the world. You look around and previously insignificant little details of nature, like the yellowing leaves on a tree, seem uncommonly beautiful. There's something deeply reassuring about those leaves: seasons come and go, the world renews, life moves on, stuff like that. For some reason even the same air seems fresher. And that apple tastes like . . . wow, have you ever tasted such a delicious apple?

Maybe you can recall what happened next.

At the first traffic snarl on the way back from the airport or the retreat centre, twinges of edginess return. It's okay, though. They just remind you of how you might have felt at another time. Then you pull into your street and discover someone has parked across your driveway, blocking your entrance. The edginess becomes more pronounced but you cope, because you have this great reservoir of I've-been-away-from-it-all peacefulness to sustain you.

Even the next morning when the alarm fails to sound, you are still coping. Same when you get stuck in the queue at the bus stop, and when the elevator gets jammed between floors at work. This getting-away-from-it-all is powerful stuff. You know the world is testing you, however. So all day long you cling to your calm feeling with all your might. You purposely slow down when the rest of the world is determined to race, you speak softly when others want to shout, you struggle to think positive thoughts when others are complaining. And just as you are thinking you might be able to pull it off, an incompetent workmate lets you down badly. *Crash*. In an instant, all that good work has gone. In its place is not only unrest and disharmony, but disappointment. By the end of the day you're back to 'normal'. It is as if you've never been away.

How does peacefulness evaporate so quickly? You start the week feeling calm and together, certain that you will be able to hold onto that feeling for ages to come, yet within a day or so it's disappeared. As if you had never even done the course. Most people who take restorative breaks come to the same realisation: the benefits are fleeting. The beauty fades, the peacefulness frays, the insights seem remote and all that space you thought was there seems to evaporate.

Calm: No Matter What is about making these qualities last. Not just for a few hours or days, or for a particular phase you are going through, but for your whole life. Right up until your very last breath.

Although it's not our primary intention, the attention-grabbing part of what follows is the way it helps you to overcome setbacks and problems. It won't prevent them, of  course, but it can certainly lessen their impact. You'll be better able to deal with pressure when you're fortified by a composure and centredness that always keeps you on track. You'll be able to bounce right back if you go off the rails at any time. When challenges come along, now you will have the ability to respond in the most constructive way. When disaster strikes, you will be able to get back to normal (the *new* normal) much faster than would otherwise be the case. And when things appear at their bleakest, you will have this inner stillness to call on, which will help you through.

For this to work you need a foundation of calm and stability that you can tap into at any time: not only when you want to feel relaxed, but when you're active and under the pump.

Peace of mind in today's world

Everyone has a theory as to why the world is restless and stressful. And why unhappiness, dissatisfaction, depression and other mental health issues are on the rise. Some say it's because we lack spiritual resources. Or discipline. Or moral fibre. Or a sense of community. Others say we're being too introspective. Or our values are changing. And some insist that this is the price we have to pay to survive in an ever-more-competitive world.

Maybe there is substance to these theories. Maybe the world is more stressful. Maybe we are feeling more anxious and depressed. Maybe some organic or spiritual change is producing all those mental health issues that concern us. On the other hand, maybe not.

There is also a strong possibility that the world is pretty much as it has always been, and we are just looking at it differently. It's possible that it is just being presented to us in a different way, and we're receiving more troubling news than we used to. It's also possible that mental health issues are as they have always been, and we are just observing or measuring them differently.

It doesn't really matter one way or the other, because you can't change the world, the people around you or, for the most part, even the immediate issues that cause you pain. All you can change is the way you look at things. But you already knew that, didn't you? Every self-help promoter in the universe seems to be peddling the same story. The problem with that claim, though, is that it's only fantasy for most of us. We can't change the way we view things. Our mental habits are too ingrained.

Now consider this: what if there was a way of developing a continuous sense of inner calm and stability without having to learn anything new or change anything old? What if there was a way of insulating yourself from life's pressures and setbacks so you would recover from them quickly and not suffer any long-lasting pain? What if there was a way of experiencing a deep level of contentment that didn't require any change in your behaviour or the way you look at things?

You'll be pleased to know there is. That's what this book is about. And most remarkable of all, what I propose involves no effort on your part. It requires commitment, for sure, but no effort.

How are you feeling right now?

The impatient side of you might like to be able to turn the page and read about a little routine that instantly transforms the way you feel: from feeling uptight and scratchy to feeling peaceful and contented, in an instant. Or from feeling jaded and lethargic to feeling enthusiastic and full of wonder. Also in an instant. While they may seem like attractive propositions, and are achievable, they won't serve you as well as what I am about to share. At least not in the longer term. Because those transformations are only about feelings.

'What's wrong with that?' you may think. 'If he could help me feel calm and relaxed, I'd be on cloud nine.' Feeling calm is relatively easy to achieve. Making it sustainable is another story. However, I want to take you further than what you feel. There are reasons for this. First, emotions are transient: whatever you are feeling will eventually morph into another feeling. Second, feelings are unreliable: they can be manipulated, overwhelmed by circumstances, and are nowhere near as logical as some psychologists pretend. The third reason is the most intriguing: it is possible for you to experience your own emotions more objectively than is generally thought – actually witnessing them arise and fade – without being bound to them, and without being unnecessarily influenced by them. The method covered in the second part of this book can enable this.

Feelings have a role to play because they help determine what you see as the quality of your existence. If at any given moment you are feeling unloved, anxious, tense, overworked, unhappy, afraid, depressed, sad, disappointed, jealous, angry, confused, embarrassed, unappreciated, wronged, dissatisfied or frustrated, you will rate your quality of life as relatively bleak. No matter what rational assessment you come up with, no matter how optimistic your attitude was at other times, right then you would consider life to be gloomy.

And if you were to experience a succession of such feelings – say feeling unappreciated which led to you feeling angry, and that leading to regret, which led to shame, which turned into fear, which drew you into a depressed like state – your life would seem even gloomier still. This is not an exaggeration; how often do negative feelings seem to be following on from one another, even when things have been going well?

The self-help people assure you that you can change the way you feel, but we all know that there are times when you don't have the presence of mind to do anything other than hang on and see where it takes you.

Now I want to present you with an alternative, a direct contrast to the negative states above. This time we're not talking about a feeling as such – at least not one that is easy to describe like joy or confidence – but more a state of mind or a quality of life. It is called equanimity.

In the classic sense equanimity means inner calmness and composure, particularly in challenging situations. Wikipedia describes it as being 'a state of psychological stability and composure which is undisturbed by experience of or exposure to emotions, pain, or other phenomena that may [upset] others'.

In some Eastern teachings equanimity is described as being one of the four sublime states (the other three being kindness, compassion and sympathetic joy). Think of it as a quiet contentedness; a sense that, no matter what is going on around you, all is okay or turning out okay. When equanimity is present, everything feels perfect.

With a foundation of calm and equanimity, you are a powerful person. It doesn't matter what feelings you are experiencing because you are aware of their transience. They come, they go, but you continue with the sense that all is okay. Deep down you are *certain* that everything is okay.

Before we move on from feelings, there is one more thought I want to leave you with. You will *feel* more peaceful and together as a result of using the process in the pages ahead. Take that as a given. Yet this is only a byproduct. The process is designed for something deeper and more fundamental than what you feel. We're aiming for a bedrock of calm and order that you will be able to depend on, no matter what challenges arise, no matter what you may be feeling at any particular moment. And, all things being equal, you'll be able to depend on this for the rest of your life.

The time and place to find equanimity

Here is an easy choice you can make that will ensure whether your experience of the world is positive or negative, peaceful or restless. That choice is where you direct your attention.

Although this is not quite as straightforward as choosing whether to look at the vase of flowers or the garbage bin, the choice I'm going to point out is many times more effective. Don't be fooled by its simplicity; it works.

Most restlessness and all negative frames of mind relate to either the past or the future, not to the present. Negative emotions such as fear and anxiety are future-based; they relate to what *may* happen. And negative emotions like regret and disappointment are past-based; they relate to what *has* happened. Future tense, past tense. No exceptions. What both have in common is that they are conceptual, existing only in your thoughts, with no concrete reality of their own. So as long as you avoid thinking forwards or backwards (which you can't do forever, obviously), you will avoid negative emotions. And, in the main, you will avoid restlessness.

Contrasting this is what occurs when all of your attention is fixed on the present. For a start, those negative frames of mind vanish. Gone. Next, the positive frames of mind that I have been writing about – stillness, peace of mind, clarity and equanimity – spring to life. If you quieten your thoughts and just experience the present, those qualities are automatically there. But the moment you start thinking about what's happening, comparing or trying to evaluate it, it's gone again. Because, by trying to get your head around what you are experiencing, you move away from the present.

Not everything to do with the past or future involves negative emotions – for example, you can have pleasing memories about past events and you can have uplifting thoughts about what you are planning to do in the future – but negative emotions cannot exist when your attention is focused on the present.

At any given moment you get to choose the attributes that determine your quality of existence. You can direct your

PAST   **FUTURE**   **PRESENT**

restlessness
can only exist here

stillness
peace of mind
equanimity
clarity

regret	*fear*	
disappointment	*worry*	*emotions are not*
shame	*doubt*	*analysed*
attachment	*desires*	

thoughts to the past or future, with the restlessness that entails, or you can direct your attention to the present and experience calm and equilibrium. These are your options: tension on one side, peacefulness on the other. Choose.

I bet you're thinking that commonsense and reason could play a more important role here. For example, if someone knows certain mental behaviours produce restlessness or undesired emotions, surely they can avoid this by modifying the mental behaviours. Here are the two things I know about such an ambition: (a) most people believe they have this ability; and (b) most people don't have this ability.

Ask any advertising researcher. Consumer interviewees invariably insist that their rationality will overcome any emotional impulses they might experience, yet they respond emotionally almost every time. This is why some people pay ten times as much for a Ferrari as they do for a Toyota. And why others pay ten times as a much for one brand of eyeliner versus another. And why people still take up smoking. And it may even be why someone who is feeling depressed about their weight chooses to eat ice-cream rather than apples.

Not convinced? Here's a little test for you: what motivates people to go to work each day? You think there's a logical answer. Surely the motivation is to earn money so they can satisfy their basic human needs for food, shelter and so on. But a recent study of over 10,000 working people revealed that the primary motivator was not financial, but emotional: the feeling of advancing towards a meaningful goal.

It's possible that you have the rare ability to overrule what you are feeling by applying reason – but just in case you do not, or that ability fails you some days, I have something more powerful you can use. We'll come to this shortly.

❦

UNDERSTANDING THE PRESENT

Now you have a fairly conventional explanation of what you experience in the present. When your attention is focused here your experiences, emotions, relationships and appreciation of the world are at their most fulfilling. Everything falls into place. You feel complete.

Perhaps there have been times when you thought that is exactly where you were – in the present – yet didn't experience anything like what I described. The critical word there is 'thought'. What you think has an influence over what you experience. Let me explain.

If you view the present as most people do – thinking that 'this moment' and 'now' have a relationship with the passage of time – you will always be looking for that gap between past and future. As logical as that seems, the present cannot found there. Why not? Logic tells you that time is linear, stretching out behind and ahead (before and after), with the future becoming the present becoming the past. According to this view, 'now' is something like an infinitesimally brief interval that's constantly updating itself. Logic may even suggest that you can string together millions of little nanosecond 'now' moments to create one continuous present. But you can't rationalise the present like that, you can only experience it. Any direct effort to grasp it in some way takes you further and further away from it.

(Yes, I am aware that I, too, have associated the present with time by comparing it with past and future. I apologise for this shortcoming of language.)

Maybe you have a more sophisticated viewpoint than the one just outlined, perhaps having come to the understanding that this moment has no relationship with time. You think you're on the right path here, but all you've done is come to the second obstacle, the one that relates to knowledge.

If you are relying on what you *know* as 'the present', you will always be trying to align what you are experiencing with what you think it should be. That's an impediment to your experiencing it. Indeed, every thought and concept that is in your head right now is an obstacle. If you think that the present is something that can be understood, rather than a reality to be experienced, you face an obstacle. If you think you have some control over the process that brings the present to you, or you to it, you face an obstacle. Same, too, if you think there is anything you can do to summon it, or if you think that you can *learn* how to be present, or think you can *perform* this practice called mindfulness. Even the subtlest notion that you have any say in what is happening or what's going to happen is an impediment.

The challenge for now is just to accept that we're dealing with something that has no intellectual, psychological or emotional component. I've been referring to it as an experience, but it's not an experience *of something*: it is just pure, unmediated awareness.

You will be pleased to know that coming up is a process that brings this to life.

By the way, if you find this whole topic of past-future-present a bit perplexing, don't lose sleep over it. Meanings and explanations have nothing to do with it.

No effort
required

Calm wherever you go

The place you find an ongoing sense of inner calm is generally much closer than where you will be looking. It's right here in the present. The obstacle that prevents you from observing this, or experiencing this, is the restless nature of your thoughts.

What if we approach from another direction? An ongoing sense of inner calm can also be found in stillness. Guess what prevents you from experiencing real stillness: the restless nature of your thoughts. You think this restlessness is caused by something else – other people, work demands, difficult circumstances, noise pollution, neuro-chemicals, past lives, cosmic vibrations or even the alignment of the planets – but you know what really causes it? The fact that your thoughts seldom rest in the present.

The question is, how can you change this? The fact that the restlessness is all about what's in your head might suggest that the solution lies in the same place. Seems logical. Just learn how to moderate what you think or feel. Quieten your thoughts, change your feelings. Certainly great swathes of society share this view. The limitation of such a strategy is that there is no psychological magic bullet that is both long-lasting and does all you want it to do. You might learn how to deal with stress and train yourself to dispassionately observe the ebb and flow of emotional states, and you might be counselled on how to deal with anger, jealousy, guilt or grief, but in the final wash-up these are temporary psychological adjustments, not permanent solutions.

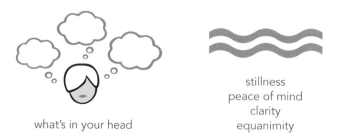

what's in your head

stillness
peace of mind
clarity
equanimity

Before psychologists and counsellors started assuming responsibility for the wellbeing of our mental states, there were religions and miscellaneous schools of philosophical thought. Their way of dealing with restlessness and misery was to overlay purpose and meaning. They say restlessness is caused by *karma*. Or it is a test of faith. Or it stems from attachments to worldly things. Or it is brought about by a weakness in your devotion to God. This meant they also had to offer solutions: you can offer up all the suffering for the greater good; you can take your mind off your own problems by practising karma yoga, or compassion, or devoting your life to the service of others. Or more extreme: you can throw yourself at the mercy of God and let Him sort it all out; or you can shrug your shoulders and say, 'It's in the stars, there's nothing I can do about it.' So it goes. Having strong beliefs and life purposes certainly worked for many, and still does to a degree, but it requires both conviction and commitment.

Despite their disparity of approach, many of those religions and schools of philosophical thought used a similar spiritual tool. Sometimes it was one of their core practices, other times it was a barely noticeable add-on. This tool or practice was known by many different names, but is mostly known as meditation. Unlike many other practices used by those religions and schools, this one produced extraordinary results without intellectual input: it removed the restlessness, it brought peace of mind, and in many ways it put the miseries of everyday life into a manageable context. And despite the best attempts of teachers to overlay meaning and purpose on this practice, it survived more or less intact for thousands of years.

Today meditation is variously presented as a peace-maker, an integral part of spiritual practice, a stress-reducer, a cure for life-threatening illnesses, a consciousness-changer, an awakening-producer, and the panacea for an extraordinary number of life's emotional, spiritual and physical ills. So much to live up to.

There was a time when I believed it could fulfil most of those claims – for everyone. My understanding was shaped by my own experiences and by extrapolating on the experiences of other meditators in my circle. However as my circle widened to include more and more diverse groups from around the globe, it became apparent that meditation – as it was widely taught – could not do all things for all people. It was also obvious that there was a huge gap between what was being offered in the classical approaches and the needs of an everyday person leading an everyday life.

An everyday person leading an everyday life. As mundane as that description may be, it accounts for most of us. Our needs vary, but are often shaped by a similar viewpoint: we have too many interests and responsibilities and too little time to focus on them – which means nowhere near enough time to commit to the rigours of a classical meditation approach.

Obviously some will disagree with my assessment, but it's pretty easy to see how most of the great meditation traditions are designed for monastic-type environments. For people who could extract themselves from day-to-day living pressures, could find the time and motivation for long periods of reflection. And because the methods were mostly cultivated within spiritual movements over hundreds or even thousands of years, they come with rituals, explanations, myths and meanings that may have little usefulness or relevance to today's user. The world these skills were designed for is light years away from everyday life today.

If you want to see how an everyday person fares with the classical offerings, do an intensive meditation course or attend a retreat. These often take place over a few days in a protected environment – peaceful, removed from worldly distractions, and with a spiritual or reflective ambience. In such an environment it is not uncommon for an everyday person to experience depth and serenity in their meditation.

Naturally they resolve to continue practising every day. Yet within days of having returned to their everyday life, the retreat is a distant memory and their resolution has faded. The practice that came so easily there now seems beyond their grasp.

My intention is not to dissuade you from attending meditation retreats, which do serve a useful restorative purpose and help consolidate your practice. I just want to highlight the difference between what is encouraged and what usually is accomplished.

You've probably guessed by now that some of what's coming up is based on meditation. What I have for you is the distillation of a number of classical meditation methods, trimmed into **a single approach that will suit a contemporary lifestyle**. I don't suggest it is superior or inferior to the others, but my approach requires no particular skill-sets, beliefs, viewpoints or commitments. (If you are already using another method it should dovetail with what's ahead.)

It's taken thirty-odd years of teaching and research to be able to say what works best in the world we live in, as opposed to the world some monk lived in 1000 years ago. One of my earliest observations of formally taught practices was that many of their trappings existed for historical or habitual reasons rather than practical. What should be focused on, and what left out? And what was the fastest way to transfer the subtle abilities of a long-term meditator to a complete novice? The answers are in the pages ahead.

Before we head there, let me share a story about mindless adherence to tradition that happened centuries ago. Every time the monks sat to meditate the monastery cat would wander in and disturb them. So the abbot told the novice to tie the cat to a tree so the monks could meditate in peace. Many years later, the old man dies, the novice is promoted to abbot, and the cat dies as well. The first thing the new abbot does is send out for a new cat to tie to the tree – so they can meditate in peace.

> It's taken me all my life to learn what **not** to play.
> Dizzy Gillespie

Sometimes ritual is part of the ambience, and can work for some people. So determining what to keep and what to leave out can be a challenge.

I recall one occasion in the eighties when I was criticised for taking too simplistic an approach to meditation in one of my books. While I was wrestling with this issue I met a prominent martial arts teacher as we were waiting to go onto a television chat show. He was a master of several martial arts, and had developed a new combat approach for the modern world. Discarding the formalistic add-ons, as well as moves and practices that served no effective purpose, he then perfected what remained. The result was a powerful new martial art that many of the leading martial artists of the day came to study with him. Something similar happened in the fifties when actor–martial artist, Bruce Lee, began training martial artists in 'the style of no style'. I took comfort from the fact that those men were criticised for abandoning tradition, even though their methods were demonstrably more effective.

Unlike martial arts, there have been very few new developments in meditation practice for the past few hundred years. Primarily, we do it the same way people have always done it. Sure there is a range of different schools, teaching fairly similar methods, each subtly suggesting that their approach is superior to others. And maybe this helps the student to feel they belong, and convinces them that there is something very special about what they've learned. Maybe this is the motivation they need when the benefits alone are not sufficient. But does this motivation last a lifetime? Not in my observation.

That's why I have spent so long streamlining my approach. The result is relatively generic, but very easy to learn and to put into action. I can't tell you how many times I have been warned that there is no commercial benefit in promoting genericism. In the words of one of my tour organisers in the USA, 'We're not going to get rich telling people that anyone could teach them this stuff.' The reality, however, is that a lot of what you get in a conventional meditation package is window-dressing, and most practices are fundamentally the same. On top of that most of them can be mastered in a few minutes.

So why is meditation presented as something that needs a teacher? I like to think of it the same way as I think of music. There comes a time when you have to stop studying and talking about it, and just get out there and play. The jazz great Charlie Parker put this in perspective when he encouraged musicians to 'master your instrument, master the music, then forget all that bullshit and just play'.

The one purpose of meditation

I will preface this by saying there are many different views of what meditation is supposed to be or do. Some people think of it as a sacred ritual akin to prayer or worship. *I don't.* Some think it has spiritual qualities in its own right. *It doesn't.* Some think it is something mysterious and transcendental. *I don't* (although I may have suggested something along those lines in earlier books).

Meditation practice has only one purpose. That purpose is not to still the thoughts so you can be in touch with the divine, or to transcend the ego, or to realise the Self, or to tap into some higher level of consciousness. The purpose is to train the attention to rest in the present.

You mean that's all? That is a big achievement. When the attention rests in the present, and there are no thoughts about the past or the future, you experience a profound inner stillness. You perceive with great clarity. And no matter what is going on around you, you sense that everything is in order.

You may wonder why you need to *train* the attention to rest in the present. Couldn't you do that of your own accord? Unfortunately not. The activity of a normal brain during a normal waking moment is, well, active: always on the move, restlessly flitting from one thought or observation to another, without any intention on your part.

Now, here's the rub. All of those thoughts going through your head are coming from or heading somewhere – into the past or the future – reviewing what has happened, comparing with past experiences, and speculating about 'what might happen if'. Note I did not say most of your thoughts, I said all of them. That is the nature of thought: always projecting or reflecting, never resting in the present where there is no movement of thought. (The experience of the present cannot be thought about, analysed or compared with any other event; you can only review it after it has passed.) This means negative frames of mind are always past- or future-based. While the act of thinking this way doesn't create the pressure, it creates the mental environment where it can arise.

Let's not forget, though, that avoiding the negative is not the game we're in. It's having the positive experience of calm and equanimity. That is why our focus is on training the attention to rest in the present.

Some people have another view about the role of meditation. Rather than training the attention, as I contend, they think its role is to *entrain*. In nature a rhythm that causes another another rhythm to gradually synchronise with it is called entrainment. Certain musical patterns like chanting and drumming, or repetitive physical patterns like dance or long train trips, can *entrain* brainwave patterns to produce meditative-like states. So entrainment may be part of the process (in some forms of meditation), but that's all it is: part of the process.

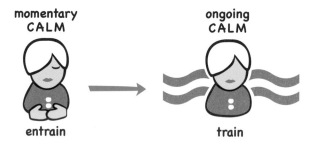

Entrainment works for producing momentary calm, but training the attention is essential if you would like a sense of calm that sticks with you for life. That's why traditional meditation practices are structured and repetitive, and why practitioners are urged to meditate at specific times on a regular basis. Training the attention to rest in the present was always its core purpose. It still is.

How meditation enhances everyday life

Each of us has a different slant on what everyday life is. It's a world of endlessly competing interests, responsibilities and priorities. A world of earning a living, raising children and maintaining relationships. A world of tip-toeing your way through local, national and even international stresses.

While we might have differing views on what constitutes everyday life, we all agree on what it is *not*: that is a peaceful, protected environment of reflection and quiet. Exactly what many meditation practices were originally designed for.

A meditation approach for everyday life, then, would need to tick a number of boxes:

- ✔ It should be easily understood and implemented.
- ✔ It shouldn't require any significant change of attitude or lifestyle.
- ✔ It should integrate with your everyday activities.
- ✔ It shouldn't take up too much time.
- ✔ It should make restlessness disappear.
- ✔ It should help you cope with everyday pressures.
- ✔ It should serve you for the rest of your days.

No surprise that what we're going to cover in the pages ahead ticks all of those boxes. However, the one that probably stands out for you is coping with everyday pressures.

There are times when you are a happy, contented, settled, peaceful, whole person. Life is rosy, health good, relationships harmonious and everything seems in order. Providing you don't think about it, you have the sense that this could go on forever. Of course it never does. Your old problems and frustrations soon come back into the picture, and you're as unsettled as ever.

These problems and frustrations are seldom big life stresses such as not knowing where your next meal is going to come from or losing a loved one. Rather they're middle-ranking aggravations like rising prices, missed appointments, noisy neighbours, difficult relationships and inconsiderate bosses. These not only stimulate negative emotions, but inject a level of restlessness to your entire worldview.

Your impulse is to try to change or remove what is aggravating you. You soon discover this is not possible. Now what are you going to do?

Maybe you do what the lifestyle magazines suggest and try to change the way you view what is aggravating you.

When you consider that most life pressures are creations of the mind – the events themselves are rarely positive or negative, it's how we perceive them that makes them seem that way – it seems logical that you can change your perceptions and turn a negative into a positive.

Let's put it to the test.

You're an intelligent, resourceful person. Have you ever succeeded in using your reasoning powers to change the way you feel about even the smallest things that are happening around you? Have you ever succeeded in making an ugly personal confrontation seem pleasant? Have you ever succeeded in making a high-stress occasion seem light and carefree? Or in transforming twitchiness into peacefulness using your willpower? If you have managed this, you've done well, but it would have been rare. Altering a viewpoint by simply using willpower or the intellect is difficult, if not impossible, for most of us.

Yet if you have a sense of calm and equanimity as your foundation, you can bring complete objectivity to whatever's before you by using a simple technique.

It's in a chapter ahead. The circumstances of the situation remain the same, your emotional response can still be the same, but deep down you take it all in your stride. The restlessness vanishes.

In some ways it's like how a good therapist can really focus on a patient's tale of suffering – listening with empathy and understanding, and often sharing in the pain they are feeling – yet let go of it all the instant they focus on the next patient.

Thinking up restlessness

You don't have to subdue restlessness, you replace it with equanimity. You don't have to avoid negative emotions, you just enjoy or endure them as the case may be, without being unduly affected by them. This is how it is when your attention rests in the present.

Trying, trying

This is fine in theory, but in practice when you are trying to keep your attention in the present, your thoughts run amok. An annoying level of restlessness, which you don't usually notice in the ferment of daily living, now asserts itself. Were you always this unsettled? Where did that come from?

Maybe you're just 'the type'. Psychologists like to talk about the Big Five personality traits (openness, conscientiousness, extraversion, agreeableness, neuroticism), and believe some of these indicate a susceptibility to restlessness. Approaching this from an entirely different direction, Buddhists say there are five mental factors that interfere with your meditation and also happen to be the root cause of most psychological problems. They call these the Five Hindrances: desire via the senses, ill-will, torpor (dullness, lack of energy), restlessness or worry, and doubt.

I have a simpler viewpoint. For the sake of symmetry, I'll continue that Five theme from above.

We have seen how restlessness originates from a specific mental activity: thinking forwards ('How will I be able to afford the rent after buying that Versace jacket?') and thinking backwards. ('Why did I spend my rent money on that jacket?') Thinking forwards or backwards are the prerequisites for unrest, but not the cause. For this we need what I call a restlessness agent. There are five of these:

- The filters we apply.
- Our urge to create order.

- Our perceptions of time.
- Our perceptions of space.
- Focus promiscuity.

〰〰〰 THE FILTERS WE APPLY. We like to think life has a level of concreteness that everyone sees the same way. That's not how it is. If another driver in the parking lot starts cursing you, you naturally assume all witnesses are seeing what you are seeing: an aggressive man with no parking manners. But only some people see this. One onlooker sees assertiveness, not anger, because she thinks the other driver was entitled to the parking space, not you. Another onlooker hates Lexus drivers and you happen to be driving a Lexus . . . you know what she's going to be thinking. As for the little old lady who was heading towards the parking space before both of you, she thinks you and the other driver are similarly offensive. Same situation, many different viewpoints.

This is the way it is for all of your experiences in life. You interpret them through a complex filter of beliefs, expectations, biases and preferences. So the head-banging music that your teenage son finds so enjoyable is stressful for you. The direct language that your boss uses is valued by other executives, but you find it pushy and abrasive. To you, the cold breeze coming through your bedroom window is fresh air; to your partner, it's a draught.

These filters play a greater role in defining what is real or pressing for you than the event or circumstance itself.

OUR URGE TO CREATE ORDER. No matter how clever we are or what philosophical outlook we favour, we see life in a linear fashion: a world of measurements, progressions, meanings and points that connect. We can accept the arguments that life is not linear and that the universe is inherently chaotic, but our hearts still think order can be found. So we look for patterns and meanings in what we encounter, we think justice should prevail, we believe that everything that occurs has an underlying cause or purpose, we believe all questions have answers, and that all events and narratives have a beginning, middle and an end.

Scratch the surface and you find that most of us harbour romantic views about order – good triumphs over evil, crime does not pay, there is a direct relationship between cause and effect, negative thinking leads to serious illness, past incarnations account for certain behaviours, *karma* rebalances and harmonises life, good princesses live happily ever after, and the like.

Whether the impulse to want this is conscious or unconscious, it encourages us to search for order where none exists. Or to cling to it when we think it exists.

The impulse manifests in other ways as well. You will be familiar with the sense of security that comes from feeling you have control over your environment. This need is so ingrained that you will suffer stress and discomfort in inverse proportion to the amount of control you believe you have in your immediate world. You feel anxious and frustrated when you have to perform repetitive tasks, when you feel you lack choices, and when circumstances force you to respond in ways not to your liking. Even when it's obvious that what you are attempting will lead to restlessness and frustration, you still try to manage events so they unfold in a predictable fashion, or to control the attitudes of others so they align with your own, or to retain what you have in the vain hope that order can be preserved.

'I am not a control freak,' you protest; 'I am co-operative and consensus-driven . . . blah blah.' That may be, but our efforts to control are more subtle than we realise. Even the need for resolution in events, stories, relationships and so forth is an innate attempt to impose order. Same when we have an expectation that people should act, or things happen, in a certain way.

When you try to exert control over the natural ebb and flow of life, you end up disappointed. Because as far as we can determine, order cannot be preserved; it gives way to chaos in a fairly predictable fashion.

This brings us to one of the great realisations of meditation: you have no control over its flow or outcome. In fact your meditation doesn't begin until you accept this. Until you accept that you have no conscious control over the content or direction of your thoughts, emotions and sensations – that you can't force yourself not to think of certain things, not to experience certain sensations, or even to remain focused on any one thing. No amount of willpower or intellectual effort will make it possible, and no amount of training will change this. This is the delicious paradox about meditation: in order to achieve what you wish or intend to achieve, first you have to give up trying to achieve it.

Here's another paradox: not only does meditation produce a satisfying state of mind and feeling of inner peace,

it is also accompanied by a profound sense of order and control.
How neat is that!

✳✳✳✳ OUR PERCEPTIONS OF TIME. As well as having a romantic view of order, we also have one of the abstract quality known as time. Abstract? We are intimately familiar with time and are greatly affected by it, but seldom pause to think what it really is. Poets can wax on about the seamless progress of existence from the past to the future, but in reality time is just a measurement of the interval between

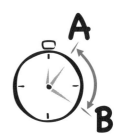

one event and another. Start your stopwatch when you leave 'A', stop it when you reach 'B', add up all the ticks in between and there you have it: time. Just a calculation. What's unsettling or disruptive about that?

Nothing. At least there would be nothing if that's where we left it, but as we mature we turn that measurement into an emotional pressure. It wasn't always like this. If you can remember back to childhood, you might recall having only a distant relationship with time; you'd be so engrossed in what was in front of you that you'd hardly notice the transition from one event to the next. But as you progress to adulthood you start to turn the abstract into the real. You start thinking of time as being something concrete, as something that can exert pressure. Once this habit begins, the restlessness sets in.

Think about this logically and you conclude that it is impossible for time to exert pressure. No matter how you crunch the numbers, there are always those same 60 little man-measured intervals in what we describe as a minute. No pressure in that.

Once you start down the logic track you might wonder if the world really is getting busier – as we all seem to think it is – or whether it is just perception. A learned behaviour. Use all the logic you like, but you still end up with the feeling that you're either running out of time or there's just not enough of it to accomplish what you have to do. Complicating this is the psychological phenomenon that the more stressed you feel, the less time you believe you have to do things. Isn't human nature interesting?

This brings us to another of the great realisations of meditation: there is no sense of time involved. If you do have any sense of time, it can only be because you're not focused on the present and your thoughts are reflecting – 'How long have I been sitting here?' – or projecting – 'How long till this finishes?' Past or future. Time has no meaning in the present. Just as there are no responsibilities, deadlines or expectations in the present. Here you are wholly aware of, and open to, what you are experiencing, but cannot compare it with anything you've experienced before (looking back) or evaluate it in terms of what you might experience in the future (looking forward). This is why they say there can be no right way or wrong way when it comes to meditation: if you are meditating there is only . . . this.

What a relief. No room for time pressure, anxiety, fear, doubt, worry (all future-based), and no room for guilt or regret (past-based). The notion of 'from this moment on . . .' is inconceivable. The belief that 'something needs to happen before . . .' never arises. Everything is happening from an innocent, unconditioned, unmediated viewpoint. Yes, what a relief.

⋀⋀⋀⋀⋀ OUR PERCEPTIONS OF SPACE. Like time, space is an abstract concept. Mathematicians and astro-physicists may have a different view, but most of us think of it as having a negative quality: the absence of something, the interval or gap between one thing and another. The missing part.

However, as life gets busier and more complex, and we imagine the spaces between the events of our day to be shrinking, we start to think of space as having a *positive* quality. Now we see it as one of those elusive, restorative moments between efforts and events.

If people think of space in that positive way, why don't they go to greater lengths to seek it out? Instead, the opposite seems often the case: they become so locked in to the stimulations and distractions of everyday living that when the occasional gap does appear – a space – they think something is missing (negative again), and the gap should be filled.

You will see the similarities in the way we view space and the way we view time: both abstract, and both endowed with more meaning than they warrant. The similarities continue when you put these in a meditation context. When you're meditating, time fades from your awareness – yet you feel you have all the time in the world. Also when you're meditating, space (if you think of it as what separates one thing from another) fades from your awareness – yet you have the feeling you are surrounded by space.

There is one more feature of space that you will discover in the latter part of this book – in the chapter called Making It Permanent. This is devoted to finding ways to 'add' more space in your day.

WWWW FOCUS PROMISCUITY. Promiscuity can relate to any behaviour that is indiscriminate or lacking in standards of selection. *Focus promiscuity* is when you habitually allow your attention to flick from one stimulus to another rather than focusing on the one thing, or series of things, that is important to you.

Many observers believe our capacity for being able to mentally focus is in decline, and attention spans are shrinking. While this may be pretty apparent in younger generations, it is also affecting the rest of us.

There are all sorts of theories as to why this might be the case. The web throws up many variations on this statement: *'we are exposed to more new information/data/mediated messages in one day than our great-grandparents were exposed to in a year'.* Extrapolated, these are suggesting that the weight of information overloads our ability to process it, and therefore adds to the pressure of daily existence. As evidence, they say the average First World adult spends somewhere between six and nine hours in front of a screen each day (a statistic that varies from country to country), the average teenager sends or receives 75 text messages a day, and every second person we see in the street seems to be glancing down at a smartphone. Add to this the ubiquitous iPod, radio, and wall-to-wall advertising messages and you have an almost inconceivable amount of data, information and stimulation coming your way.

If your attention was continuously focused on changing data, or was being continuously drawn from one piece of information or news to another, that might seem like a plausible explanation for decreasing attention spans.

However, the amount of available data or information cannot be the culprit. Data has always existed. There has always been too much data for one person to attend to or absorb. Besides, the *potential* for distraction is not, in itself, a reason to indulge in it. So why do we habitually seek it out? And does this habit lead to an altered way of thinking?

I have previously written about a function of the human nervous system that is a contributor to this.

A calming system or a nervous system?

Before we go into this topic about the nervous system, there's something about the nature of all systems that needs to be kept in mind. Any system in nature – be it solar, weather or tidal system – is so complex it can never be fully understood. If you look at it one way you see a whole system, probably made up of a number of smaller sub-systems. But look at it another way, and you see just one component of a much larger system. This means we should never fool ourselves into thinking any one component tells the whole story or predictably influences the overall.

The human organism also features a number of systems. There are a dozen or so of these – reproductive, digestive, respiratory, endocrine, immune, nervous and so on. As with the systems in nature, many of these interrelate and can influence one another, and most consist of smaller sub-systems.

Okay, that's the technical part. Now we're going to take a look at one part of the nervous system, the autonomic nervous system. This operates many of your body's functions from a level below consciousness.

Broadly speaking, the nervous system consists of two parts, the *sympathetic* (the 'tense side') and the *parasympathetic* (the 'calm side').

These are not located in any specific part of the body, and they do not sit side by side – so what you see in the graphic here is a metaphor.

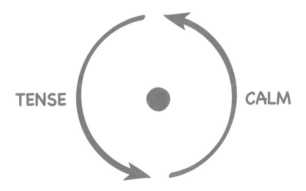

TENSE   **CALM**

The tense side and the calm side have counterbalancing actions: one starts a physiological series of events, the other stops it or compensates for it. In combination, they help you to deal with the wear and tear of everyday life.

Typically, the *sympathetic* (tense) part comes into play when some sort of stimulus makes you feel under pressure. This stimulus could be a threat (real or imagined), or it could be a primal impulse like sex or hunger. It could even be a simple action like walking up stairs, or a change in ambient temperature. A convenient way of describing one of these factors is as 'a stress'.

When a stress comes along the tense side swings into action, producing a range of excitatory neurotransmitters (the expression alone is enough to stir you up!), which results in a shock of hormones – such as adrenaline and corticosteroids – being injected into your bloodstream. These do things like speeding up the heart rate and blood flow, tensing the muscles, increasing perspiration and suspending digestion. According to the human model, you are now physically and emotionally prepared to deal with the stress.

After the sexual activity has been consummated, the speech given, the argument settled or the deadline met, the calm side, the *parasympathetic* nervous system, comes into play. Its role is to restore, balance, heal and conserve energy after all the excitement. It does this by helping you calm down, digest food and rest. It also activates the immune system and generally gets you ready to go back into action later. The calm side produces its own range of neurochemicals, such as dopamine and serotonin, which are designed to calm you down and elevate the mood. Sometimes these are no match for the chemicals produced by the other side, and are easily overwhelmed by them.

For simplicity's sake, we'll refer to this as the tense-calm cycle.

Combined, the two parts of the tense-calm cycle help you deal with an active, unpredictable life: one part preparing you for action, the other part calming you down after it has passed.

In an ideal world these two parts would remain perfectly balanced relative to the centre, the inner you. A bit like a gyroscope, where the centre remains stable regardless of any movement of the overall. So no matter what ups, downs, tilts or shifts you had to endure, everything just hangs together in perfect balance. Unfortunately in today's non-stop world, the tense–calm cycle doesn't always work so smoothly.

The diagram below broadly illustrates some of its functions and characteristics. I'd like to draw your attention to the attributes on the tense side.

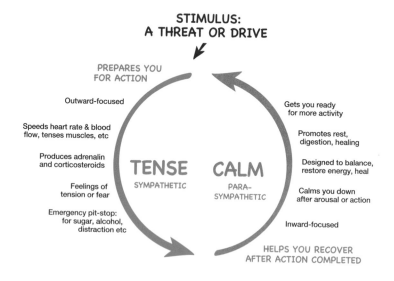

**STIMULUS:
A THREAT OR DRIVE**

PREPARES YOU
FOR ACTION

Outward-focused

Speeds heart rate & blood
flow, tenses muscles, etc

Produces adrenalin
and corticosteroids

Feelings of
tension or fear

Emergency pit-stop:
for sugar, alcohol,
distraction etc

TENSE
SYMPATHETIC

CALM
PARA-
SYMPATHETIC

Gets you ready
for more activity

Promotes rest,
digestion, healing

Designed to balance,
restore energy, heal

Calms you down
after arousal or action

Inward-focused

HELPS YOU RECOVER
AFTER ACTION COMPLETED

The tense side alters your outlook on the world. When it is activated, two things happen: (a) you become outwardly focused, looking for a broad view of what's going on, and (b) you have a diminished ability to take in detail. This is fine if you are dealing with a life-or-death issue like a rhinoceros charging your way, but what if the issue is small? Most of the stressful issues you face in life are comparatively minor: you're running late for an appointment, you have to speak in front of your workmates, or you have a deadline approaching and your figures don't add up. But if the tense side is making you less capable of handling detail, your problems are compounding. Especially when you consider that one of the most cited stresses of modern life is being bombarded with detail.

Here's another ironic characteristic of the tense side. When it has been active for some time, and you don't know how you're going to cope with all this pressure, you get the urge for an emergency pit-stop. To top up your fuel levels for the next phase of the drama.

At a primal level, this is probably just a need for carbohydrates, but in today's world of readily-available stimulants such a craving can manifest in any number of undesirable choices: sugary foods and drinks, fats, energy drinks, alcohol (for the sugar hit), drugs or nicotine.

And just as commonly, it can also lead to desire for emotional stimulation such as novelty, distraction, information or entertainment.

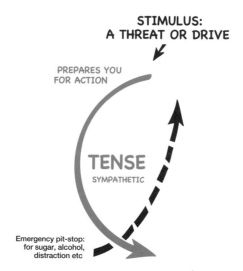

Say you give in to this urge. You drink the cola, smoke the cigarette or listen to some loud music.

As each of these has a stimulating effect on the nervous system, the tense side gets all fired up again. Your heart rate and pulse speeds up, your muscles tense, your digestion slows down, and sooner or later you feel the need for yet another emergency pit-stop to top up fuel levels. You give in to this and you have created a feedback loop and the whole cycle begins again.

Where the initial stress may have arisen from factors outside of your control, the second one – if you were to give in to it – is self-inflicted. And if you do give in to it, does it soothe things? Not at all: it aggravates, often prolonging the response. Then, instead of getting to enjoy the calming or recovery part of the cycle, you get mired in the tense side. Your heart and pulse rate remain elevated, stress hormones continue to enter your system, feelings of tension and fear do not subside. Then what do you do? You go searching for stimulation or distraction again!

My description is greatly simplified, of course, but it illustrates how a constantly stimulated nervous system could contribute to the pressure and unease you feel in today's world.

To bring this more into your day-to-day experience, think about how you feel when something stressful happens at work. Say you have an important deadline to meet. Then, out of the blue a situation arises that might slow you down – your computer crashes, you cannot get your car out of the car park or you've mislaid an important document. So much to do, so little time, now look what is happening!

The smart thing to do would be to knuckle down and work harder until the situation has been resolved. But that's not what most highly stressed people do: they check their email, make unnecessary adjustments to the layout of their spreadsheet, pour another coffee, step outside for a cigarette, reach for a biscuit or rearrange the papers that have been messing up their desk all week. There's no logic to this, and it's probably unconscious anyway, but you can see how such an impulse would compound the pressure you feel rather than ease it.

Imagine where such a tendency might lead. Assuming that life is as we believe it to be – with work, family, politics, traffic, noise and so on, growing increasingly more stressful – then all the masses of data we are confronted with not only add to the burden, but contribute to a spiralling behavioural change. The more pressure we face, the more we feel compelled to distract ourselves. Then we start to confuse stimulation with relaxation and go looking for more novel forms of stimulation in order to 'relax'. The irony is obvious: stimulation is intended to excite and titillate the senses, while relaxation is intended to soothe them; one cannot fulfil the function of the other.

The above is an instinctive process, but left unchecked it feeds upon itself and contributes to the behaviour we call focus promiscuity.

Now for a choice you know you have, but probably forgot all about

The tense part of the autonomic nervous system is energetic in nature: it gets you feeling fired up, ready for action. The calm part tends to be lethargic: you feel the urge to rest and restore.

In the modern world, when you're working flat out and your energy starts to wane, you automatically think of what you have to do to restore your energy. A carb hit. Caffeine. Distraction. Push-ups. Yet your body is telling you to sit for a moment, close your eyes, switch off. Your habit is telling you to speed up, but your body is telling you to slow down.

What if you were to follow nature, have a 5-minute catnap, and then come back to the fray? Do you think you'd feel better? Would you perform better? I know many executives who've trained themselves to do this, and who believe they are capable of much more as a result. Even if there was no improvement in performance at all, it certainly seems like a more wholesome approach to life.

Focus promiscuity

We can't blame the nervous system for our tendency to become distracted; there is more to focus promiscuity than this. In fact, I think we're witnessing an attention revolution in the making.

For example, my observation in the corporate world is that the attention habits of everyday executives have undergone a massive change in just a few decades. While some of this can be attributed to technological development: the amount of data we have access to has escalated beyond comprehension; the number of times we are presented with uninvited information multiplies each year; understandings that once came from reading several books are now gleaned from a few paragraphs on Wikipedia; the briefcase has been replaced by a laptop (containing millions of times

more data); and the 'always on' smartphone is replacing almost everything.

However, we can't put all the blame on technology because personal preference is clearly playing a role. Some obvious examples: the information that used to require a ten-page document is now preferred as a single chart; the once-sought-after quiet workplace is now viewed as unstimulating and needs to be supplemented by bold graphics and music at every workstation; wandering from department to department is replaced by clicking between menus on your browser; and for many, the boundary between office and home barely exists. You get the picture.

This change is not limited to the workplace. In your lifetime you have seen profound changes in the way an individual deals with information and learning. For example, my way of processing information is such that I can usually deal with only one source of data at a time. Contrasting this, my thirty-year-old news editor son can juggle several sources simultaneously, my twenty-year-old student son can deal with even more, and my seventeen-year-old student daughter not only contends with more than that again, but actively chooses to do so. You will see similar patterns wherever you look.

There are many theories as to why this change is taking place and why an accompanying level of distractibility may be emerging. Some believe it's just a fashion in the way we process information, or that it stems from lowered motivation or a reduction in willpower. I've even heard suggestions that it represents a decline in cognitive health, such as that associated with ageing.

More likely it is a changing – *evolving?* – human capability. We know that certain types of stimulation can change brain

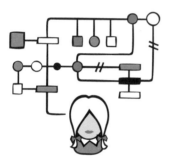

formation, a fact that can be observed by comparing the brain formation of digital-era children with the brains of their pre-digital-age parents. We also know that this can have a real effect on the way they apply their mental resources. Perhaps this has happened before. Just as the children of two hundred years ago retrained their brains to absorb information via reading (a single source), the children of today are retraining their brains to take in information in a non-linear, hypertext fashion (multiple, cross-referenced sources). Check out any classroom in the developed world.

There is little doubt that this new way of taking in information sees today's children having greatly reduced attention spans compared to those of their parents. Contrary to what many fear, though, focus promiscuity doesn't appear to make much difference to learning; research shows that children have cultivated the ability to pay attention intermittently, while absorbing just as much information as someone who is attending with more focus.

Weighing against this, however, focus promiscuity does have a couple of significant downsides. First, even when it has a strategic, information-gathering purpose, it reduces the opportunity for reflection, which is considered to be a prerequisite for perspective and wisdom. Second, focus promiscuity is almost always accompanied by feelings of unrest. There is a direct correlation between scattered attention and the biometrics you normally associate with stress. One leads to the other.

The big question is: if these changes in mental behaviour are as pronounced as they appear to be, are they in themselves sufficient to prevent you from discovering the underlying sense of inner calm and equilibrium I've been writing about?

Now let me put this information into a useful perspective for you.

Some of the world's most committed attention-observers are meditation teachers. And when you take away all their teaching whistles and balloons, you find they have only one tool to work with. Not the intellect, the emotions or the soul, but the attention.

A number of my meditation-teaching contemporaries began their service in the early seventies. Along with me, they have devoted a large part of their lives to one very narrow practice that involves not much more than stillness and focus. If ever there was a perfect vantage point for observing changes in meditators' ability from one era to the next, it is the one that we enjoy.

Our consensus is that there has been little change in the behaviour of meditators over the past thirty years. Be they fourteen years old or sixty-four, today's novice appears to be just as capable – or just as incapable – of remaining still for extended periods as the novice meditator was in 1974.

Yet, while there seems to be no discernible difference in their capacity for remaining focused, there does seem to be a difference in their *willingness* to do so on an ongoing basis. This is hardly a scientific observation, but the major difference appears to be one of perseverance rather than capability.

In other words, the novice meditator has less perseverance today.

Later in this book we will explore how you can overcome this tendency.

Training the attention

If you search for it, you will find endless discussion on the three topics of consciousness, awareness and attention.

Consciousness and awareness are perennially hot topics, yet there are no agreed definitions. Philosophers, psychologists and neuroscientists are all on completely different pages, and none of them can accurately say what either word really means. We know they are often used interchangeably, yet we believe them to have quite different qualities. Depending on your viewpoint, consciousness arises in awareness or awareness arises in consciousness. Or consciousness is an activity of the brain and awareness is the field – or is it the other way around, or somewhere in between?

You can study either topic for the rest of your life, and you won't get anywhere.

Let's just agree that you have a general idea of what the words mean, so we can shift our focus to the next word, 'attention'.

Attention is a facet of awareness or consciousness. It differs from both in that it is a reasonably well-understood cognitive process. William James, history's favourite psychologist–philosopher, described it as 'the taking possession by the mind, in clear and vivid form, of one out of what seem several simultaneously possible objects or trains of thought'. In other words, attention is when you focus on one aspect of your world while ignoring all others.

In this way attention plays a pivotal role in producing the benefit this book promises: an underlying sense of calm and equanimity.

I have previously described the inner stillness that occurs when the attention rests in the present, when there are no thoughts about the past or the future. You know you could manage this for a few seconds at a time, but certainly not on an ongoing basis. Too many distractions. Besides, even if it were possible to continually keep your attention present, why would you want to? You'd never remember where you parked the car this morning, and you wouldn't know what sort of food to buy for dinner tonight. I am not proposing an ongoing state of 'being in the present', merely suggesting that this should become your *default quality of attention*. Right now your default quality is movement – continually flitting between the past and future with all the restlessness that entails – and coming to rest in the present on only the rarest occasions. By the end of this book you will know how to reverse this, making peacefulness and stability your base. Then your forays into the past and future become activities of the present, where there is peacefulness rather than restlessness.

If you were to give this any thought right now you'd say the millions of distractions of modern life would prevent you from reaching this goal. But distraction just means that something or somebody else is determining where your attention is focused. Soon that will be you. When you, and you alone, are the one who determines where your attention is directed, distraction is much less of an issue.

It works like this: you can *entrain* the attention so that it ignores distraction and remains focused in the present for a few seconds or minutes at a time. This serves a useful purpose – like experiencing deep peacefulness and activating the calming side of the tense–calm cycle.

We will explore the process that enables this in the pages ahead. But if you're thinking long term you need to do more than entrain, you need to *train* the attention. You need to train it to rest in the present at your discretion.

How long a commitment?

Normally, to convince someone to commit to an indefinite quest like 'training the attention to rest in the present', one would need to offer a definite reward at the end, together with a bunch of identifiable milestones along the way.

If that's what you're thinking I'm afraid you have a small expectation hurdle to overcome. Because the outcome of what lies ahead is as irrelevant as the time frame. Only the process matters.

Fortunately, training the attention is a process that can be savoured and enjoyed for its own sake.

This is not just me trying to be clever. If you have an outcome in mind, it involves projecting into the future. If you have benchmarks, it involves reflecting on where you've come from. You know the drill by now: reflecting on the past or projecting into the future sets the scene for unrest. Keeping your attention in the present brings peacefulness. This process is about keeping the attention in the present.

There will be an outcome, of course. There will be change. And as a matter of interest only, there are two ways of measuring it: one internal, the other external.

The internal one is how things seem from 'the inside'. This is the only measure that counts. It relates to your personal experience, the one area where you are the expert. To what degree you will notice it varies from person to person; it may be immediate, but probably will be subtle and cumulative. Think of it as you would a physical exercise program where the benefits creep up on you. You plug along, focusing on the process rather than the outcome, immersing yourself in the routine, enjoying it for what it is rather than for what it is meant to achieve. The only change you notice is the fact that you're feeling better than you used to, and that you seem to be enjoying other aspects of life more. Then one day somebody says, 'Hey you're looking fantastic!' and all your efforts suddenly come into focus.

The external way of measuring change is far less important. And much more complex. You will have read or heard about neuroplasticity – the changes in the brain's neural pathways and synapses due to variations in behaviour, circumstances and/or mental practices. It's a popular topic that, in a broad sense, doesn't reveal much more than you've already discovered through your own experience: your habits and routines have an influence on how you experience the world around you.

What may not be so obvious, though, is that these also have a distinct influence on the physical structure of your brain. There have been well-publicised studies into what happens to the brain's structure and function as the result of extended meditation practice. (I funded some of these experiments myself in the eighties, though employing different technology to what's commonly used today.) The result of these studies was that long-term meditation changes the cortical density or thickness of what we call grey matter, as well as producing physical changes in those parts of the brain that relate to positive functions such as attention, compassion, feelings of peacefulness, emotional stability, healing and coping. Some studies showed improvements in areas that relate to negative feelings such as depression, fear and anger.

How long does it take for such changes to be observable?

It has long been held that a musician's brain permanently changes after more than 10,000 hours of practice, so early studies into meditators' brains focused on subjects who'd been meditating for similarly long periods (20–40,000 hours, or a couple of decades). No surprise that Buddhist monks were used for the initial studies. In the nineties, a psycho-neuroimmunology researcher I knew observed noticeable changes much earlier than this – after only 200 hours. More recently neuroscientists have identified structural change to the brain after only eight weeks of practice (25 hours). And some speculate that the change begins even earlier than this. Later, we will look at some research that has been conducted into the formation of habits; you might be surprised to find that this process is also shorter and more predictable than you thought.

While the above may be fascinating, all that really matters is what you observe yourself. It makes no difference whether any changes are demonstrable or independently verifiable because all that counts is your personal experience.

If you are feeling calm, no amount of data can change that.

Bringing your attention to meditation

Where you direct your attention is the greatest influence on how you experience the world.

Although your brain and body are always responding to an extraordinary range of stimuli, with a myriad of physiological responses (sweating, shivering, feeling thirsty, and so on) taking place, all that registers is what is in your field of attention.

Your attention is a fairly straightforward feature of consciousness. You notice one thing, but you don't notice others, that's how we tend to think of it. But attention comes in a number of different grades. Some play a critical role in helping you find and maintain a state of inner calm. If you ask the average thinking person to nominate these – that is, to describe the different qualities of attention that exist – they would probably narrow it down to two extremes: inattention (when you're not paying attention) and focused attention (when you *are* paying attention). Either–Or.

Meditators pay more attention to attention than most of us. So if you put the question to a meditator, they might nominate a third quality: sustained attention. Accordingly, they would describe the meditation process as being a sliding scale of awareness defined by what's happening to your attention. You start out being inattentive, then progressively become focused, more focused . . . until you are sustained in this focused place for some time.

Inattention	Focused Attention	Sustained Attention

That simplified scenario doesn't work if you're looking for a way of training the attention to rest in the present. For this we need a broader view.

There are five qualities of attention that concern us here. I call these scattered, diffuse, separate, focused and centred. (There is a sixth, a kind of third-party or surrendered attention. This is when somebody else dictates the content of your awareness, as in hypnotism, guided relaxation and meditation commentaries. However it is not something that relates to our needs right now.) If you're wondering why I don't have 'inattention' on my list, it's because this is not a quality of attention in its own right.

scattered   We'll start with the one you know best of all, the type of attention that defines your everyday awareness. One moment you're thinking about how much work you have to complete, the next you're thinking about what you're going to be having for dinner, then you're looking at the storm clouds outside the window, then you're thinking about how good looking your meditation teacher is, and so on. This is usually accompanied by a feeling of restlessness.

diffuse   Now you're more relaxed. Your attention has become hazy and dull. Some people refer to diffuse attention as a meditative state. I no longer use that term, and question whether there is such a thing as a meditative state (yes, I admit I described it this way myself in past books). Diffuse attention exists when you're glazed over, drifting, zoned out; like when you're on a long bus trip, or you're having a head massage, or maybe just daydreaming. It will soon be evident to you that this is not meditation and, despite how it seems, it is not an ideal of meditation.

separate According to the conventional view, inattention is the opposite to what we strive for in meditation. And the opposite of inattention is separateness. Let me explain.

The separateness I'm going to describe relates as much to your worldview as it does to attention, because it is the way you make sense of what's around you. The way it functions comes very naturally to you: you separate everything into a subject–object perspective. The subject is 'I' or 'me', and the object is whatever I direct my attention towards. Let's call that 'other'. Always two separate parts.

No matter how objective you try to be, you invariably end up using 'I' as the yardstick. For example, Jack is up there, Jill is down here (up and down are relative to where 'I' am). You don't set out to do this, but every observation you make ends up being subjective: there is me and my skin, me and my feelings, me and something else, me and the universe, me and eternity. At no time is there a sense of 'I' being the observer of the experience or phenomenon.

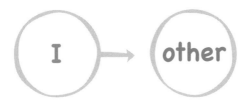

As common and as necessary as it may be, this separate way of seeing the world is where restlessness is made possible. Yet when your attention is completely focused in the present – as it is when you're meditating – the perception of separateness disappears and there is stillness. You are aware of the whole, and there is no discernible division between subject and object, between 'I' and 'other'. This perception is subtle and fleeting, and isn't something we'll be exploring in this book.

If you examine what happens in a typical concentrative meditation, you will see how the separateness disappears. You focus on something – a word, a mantra, a candle flame – until it fills your awareness. Now there is room in your awareness only for this 'object'. This means you no longer have this impression of me plus something else, there is only something else. Then the something else drops away and your attention is filled with the whole.

The same phenomenon occurs – though in a less obvious way – when your attention is fully focused on a particular activity or experience. Or, to put this another way, when it is fully focused on the present. This is complete objectivity. The classic mindfulness practices are designed to achieve this, as is the process I am going to introduce shortly.

focused   As well as being the holy grail of the classroom, focused attention is an integral part of the meditation world – although my observation is that it is often misunderstood in this context.

Whenever we think of focus in a visual context, we think of it in terms of effort. From a physical point of view, this makes sense because effort is involved. Eyesight requires a degree of muscular tension to adjust the lens so light is directed to the part of the retina known as the fovea. This brings near or far objects in the centre of your vision 'into focus', and enables the perception of depth and dimension.

However, *foveal* vision is only one aspect of vision. The remaining part of your visual field, the part that surrounds the centre, is known as *peripheral* vision. You access it by relaxing the muscles in the lens of your eyes.

You tense the muscles to bring a scene into focus, and you relax those same muscles to emphasise your peripheral vision. Tensing, relaxing.

Now refer back to the section on the tense–calm cycle of the autonomic nervous system. The tense side encourages feelings of alertness and edginess while the calm encourages relaxation. Tensing, relaxing. You've probably already guessed the link: foveal vision is linked to the tense side and your peripheral vision is linked to the calm. Tensing, relaxing.

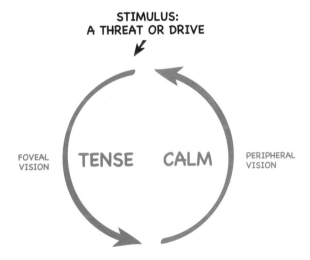

When we're talking about focus in a meditation context, the word relates to concentration more so than it does to vision. As a cognitive rather than a physical process, do you think it involves effort? Do you think it warrants the intense look, or the furrowed brow, that so often accompanies any attempt to concentrate?

Concentration is just a decision – choosing what you pay attention to – then perhaps remaking that decision on a continuing basis. If you choose to concentrate where your eyes focus, fine. But you could just as easily choose to concentrate on what is in your relaxed peripheral vision. Or maybe you choose to close your eyes altogether and just concentrate on the first thought to come to mind. It's just a decision. No effort is required.

There is another discovery you will come to. Choosing whether to concentrate on foveal vision or peripheral vision can influence the way you feel. Concentrating on your foveal vision can encourage feelings of alertness, possibly edginess, whereas concentrating on your peripheral vision can lead to feeling more peaceful and relaxed.

You can experiment with this yourself: really focus on the words on this page, then widen your peripheral vision so that you see a much wider field. At the most superficial level, the simple easing of muscular tension promotes a more relaxed feeling, but the real change is taking place at a more subtle level. Maybe this change is not immediately noticeable, but over time it begins to add up.

For now, though, the most important aspect of focused attention is the way you can use it to arrive at 'centred attention' – in a predictable and sustainable way.

centred This brings us to the quality of attention that is central to what this book offers. It's where you attentively view all experiences and observations from what I can only loosely describe as 'within the experience'. It encompasses all of the other qualities of attention in one form or another, yet **it stands alone as being the way to achieve ongoing calm and equilibrium.** While it may not seem very exotic, it is one of the easiest ways of bringing the attention to rest in the present.

And as well as being calming and spiritually energising, centred attention enables you to function at your peak.

Even though it is very accessible, it is rare for most people to apply centred attention. Ironically, those occasions seem so special that we invent names for them: mind-body connection, being in the moment, experiencing flow, and so on.

By employing a mix of *focused* attention and *centred* attention you can bypass the other distracting types of attention to experience deep, inner stillness.

Your one area of control

There's a characteristic of the different qualities of attention that you will be noticing from now on.

When you're meditating or just trying to focus the attention, you begin to realise that the attention seems to have a will of its own. It seems to be in a constant state of movement – seamlessly moving from one phase to another, without any intentional input on your part, and usually without your noticing. You have scattered attention, then moments later it becomes diffuse and you 'zone out', then it's focused, then it's diffuse, then it's back to focused . . . oops, scattered again. Accepting the fluid, almost-chaotic nature of this pattern is central to finding the stillness within it.

You can train the attention to be more orderly.

You can train it to *want* to stay resting in the present.

You can train it to be centred.

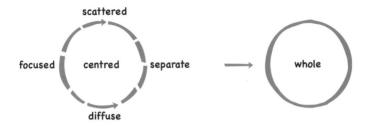

The training involves two steps.

The first involves making decisions about where to focus your attention. The second is the methodology you use to keep it centred.

Most of what you do is directed towards the first part, focusing the attention. When you have that under control – note that word 'control' – the second step is fluid and pretty much unnoticeable.

Previously, we addressed the topic of control, and how our conscious or unconscious efforts to establish order contribute to feelings of uneasiness and frustration. You avoid these by accepting that you have no control over what's going on: no control over your immediate environment, no control over your peers, your charges and subordinates, not even over your own body and mental processes. That's the most sobering of your discoveries: the fact that you have no real control over yourself. No conscious control over how you feel, what you think, the impressions you gain, or the content of your thoughts. And while you may be able to control small actions, like whether your left foot lands in front of your right foot, you have limited control over most of the way your body functions from one moment to the next.

Relax. There *is* one aspect of awareness that you do have conscious control over. Perhaps the only one . . . You can control where you direct your attention.

At any given moment you have a choice in where your attention comes to rest. You can choose to look out the window or you can choose to look at the carpet; you can choose to register the scent of the flowers or you can choose to note the temperature of the air-conditioning; you can choose to look at your broken fingernail or to think about the melting ice shelf in Antarctica. Of all the billions of potential focus points in existence, *you* choose the one. And you make this choice moment by moment. So much power and control at your disposal.

The choosing is the easy part. What is more difficult is being able to sustain your attention in that place for any length of time. Say, more than a few seconds. Yet with training you can change this. More easily than you think.

When I was a kid, there was a little attention game I used to play near an ants' nest in our paddock. I'd draw a circle in the dirt and observe any ants that walked through. The object of the game was to ignore the movement of the ant once it left the circle. Most people can't focus like that. But after a few days of playing the same game – probably for no more than ten minutes at a time – it became much easier. You can discover the same for yourself: it's easy to train the attention if you stay with it. Just as you can't lift the heavier barbells when you first start going to the gym, it soon becomes achievable; many curls later, it may even become relatively effortless. Same with training the attention. Right now you probably can't remain focused on one thing for more than a few seconds, but with a little training it becomes second nature.

I refer you back to the section on training the attention, and those studies into neuroplasticity and what happens to the physical structure and function of the brain as the result of extended meditation practice. You can call it meditation practice or you can call it training the attention, but it gradually produces an observable biological change, such as a measurable increase in the density of grey matter and variations in those parts of the brain that relate to attention.

Moreover there is evidence these changes can be observed after only a few weeks of effortless, enjoyable practice.

Let's do it

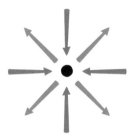

This segment will show you how to find an ongoing sense of calm and equilibrium in two easy-going phases. Both are relaxing and enjoyable.

The first involves training the attention to rest in the present. Effortlessly. The second extends that ability into everyday life. In both cases, you have a state of restful attentiveness as your centre.

Phases one and two are really one and the same: the training is the everyday life application, and the everyday life application furthers the training.

To prepare for what's ahead, take a mental snapshot of the above graphic. It is the formula to, and contains almost everything you need to know about, finding calm and equanimity in an instant.

Outwards→Inwards

Now I'm going to introduce you to the attention-training method I have personally been using for the past 40-odd years. Even though I've taught many meditation styles and techniques, and have written many books and articles about them, there is only one approach I keep coming back to. It is the essence of all meditation practices.

In the early stages of my writing career, I teamed up with a group of neuro-feedback researchers to evaluate as many different types of meditation and so-called consciousness-changing methodologies that we could find. Our aim was to determine whether meditation or other methods brought any significant benefits to the user – first purely from their subjective viewpoint, then by more objective assessment. Then we wanted to see if any of the skills they used could be streamlined and passed onto a novice in a more immediate way. What we ended up with was a grab-bag of little physical and mental behaviours that long-term meditators used, usually unconsciously, in their practice. Our theory was that by emulating these a novice could shave years off normal practice requirements.

I've written about these practices elsewhere, but will share a few now just to illustrate how easy it is to relax the body and still the thoughts in meditation.

While our interest was primarily on what people did with their minds and thoughts, their mental postures if you like, we also looked at what was happening in a physical sense. Something that quickly became obvious was that you can use physical postures, simple actions, or any of the senses to quickly alter the way you are experiencing life. For example, if you lower your eyelids now, you will feel your body start to relax. You don't have to do anything else. Try it. Lower your eyelids now.

You can easily figure out why that relaxes you the way it does. You've spent a lifetime conditioning yourself to associate the lowering of eyelids with entering a more relaxed state. You do it every night. So it's a learned association. (There may be other physiological reasons, but this one will do for the moment.)

Sometimes, though, the reason is not so obvious.

For example, if you lower your eyeline now – dropping your gaze about 45 degrees – you will feel the muscles in the

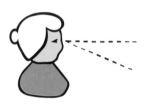

back of your neck starting to relax. Where did that come from? What's the link? I have no idea. All I know is that's how it happens. Better still, the rest of your body starts to relax

soon after. I can feel my pulse rate drop a few points after doing this for a few seconds.

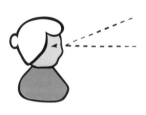

Let's try another eye movement. This time, *raise* your eyeline around 30–45 degrees – that is looking slightly upwards. You can do this with your eyes closed or open. You

may notice some physical relaxation as a result, but that's not why I mentioned it. Raising your eyes this way makes it easier to still your thoughts when you're meditating (at least it does for many). Don't ask me why this happens, it just does.

Now we can move this discussion a little further into the meditation arena. Some traditional approaches encourage you to adopt a 'soft gaze'. When you try this you notice how defocusing the eyes encourages the body to relax. (Please note: I am not suggesting you make a habit of this. A soft gaze tends to promote a diffuse attention, which as we noted earlier, is of minimal use in meditation.) A more useful way of achieving the same end is to *widen your peripheral vision* – that is, take in more visual information around you without moving your eyes. Not only does this lead to a relaxing change of state, but it also makes it easier to keep your attention focused while you are meditating. If you refer back to the section on focused attention, and the action of the autonomic nervous system, you might see a reason for this.

Exactly the same happens when you *use your peripheral hearing*.

Oh, you didn't know you had peripheral hearing? Try it out now: just listen for 'sound in general' rather than a specific sound. That's all it takes to access it.

There are dozens of these little physiological quirks that we have observed. I've even included a few in the attention-training process I'm about to share with you now.

The bare-bones approach to meditation

There is a bare-bones approach to meditation that I wish someone had pointed out when I first started studying the topic. It's based on the one aspect of life you have control over: where you direct your attention.

The formula behind it is easy to remember because it is just like breathing: you breathe in, you breathe out – inwards, outwards, inwards, outwards – and unless something happens to interrupt this, you never give it another thought. You just go with the flow, without trying to control what's happening in any significant way, and everything takes place naturally and spontaneously.

Refer back to the graphic at the beginning of this section. It sums up the entire process: inwards, outwards, inwards, outwards . . . in, out, in, out . . . with not another thing to do, understand, remember or think about. It's not a matter of what you do or don't do, what you think or don't think – all we care about is where you direct your attention. That's inwards, outwards, inwards, outwards.

In the first instance you should try what follows in a quiet, restful environment. Seated is best. Back straight, feet flat on the floor, lighting dimmed, phone turned off, and so on. You don't need music, incense or any atmospheric enhancement that you might grow to rely on.

The ideal time?

Any time works, but if your aim is to create a habit, doing this first thing in the morning is perfect. If that means rising half an hour earlier than usual, you will find that little bit of relinquished sleep is more than compensated for by the meditation. If you wish, you could put aside a similar period of time in the evening as well.

STEP 1. WHERE AM I NOW? [→ INWARDS]

This first step has a dual relevance. Directing the attention inwards works towards activating the soothing side of the tense–calm cycle. Even more soothing, it grounds the exercise in an accessible, familiar place so you will be able to make an effortless transition from 'somewhere out there' to 'here'.

You can try this step right where you are now. It relates to bringing your attention to what you perceive as your physical centre. And it demonstrates how a simple shift of attention is all it takes to encourage stillness and inner quiet . . .

Without doing another thing, just turn your attention to where your body touches the floor or the chair. There's nothing else you have to do or think about. Just direct your attention to where your feet touch the floor. Or where your body makes contact with the chair or cushion. Bring all of your attention to that place.

Now, just rest in that awareness.

Simply by nature of directing your attention to this place, you will feel the body relax and thoughts starting to slow down. Enjoy it. That's the first step.

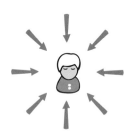

If you become aware of the subtle sensation of your body sinking into that place, just keep focusing. That sensation is neither here nor there. And if you become aware of a sense of groundedness, of being anchored in the place you are, that is neither here nor there either. All that's important is that you direct your attention here. Then rest in this awareness.

STEP 2. WIDENING THE ATTENTION [OUTWARDS→]

This is the only step that has a purpose. In fact, it has two: to momentarily change the way your brain is working so you begin easing into a more relaxed state, then to establish the potential limits of your sensory awareness. (The latter helps to prevent potential distractions from becoming distractions.)

It works like this:

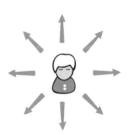

When you are feeling comfortable with Step 1, and your attention is firmly centred in the physical sensation of being grounded where you are at this moment, it's time to broaden the attention, stretching it outwards, in all directions.

You could use any of your peripheral senses for this step, but initially you will find it easier to rely on your sense of hearing. Then you can allow your eyes to slowly close – if you find that relaxing – as they are naturally inclined to do when you are unwinding.

Maintaining that sense of groundedness, of being firmly anchored in this place, use your sense of hearing to take in the broad field of your awareness.

No need to focus on anything in particular, just keep directing your attention outwards – stretching – farther and farther afield, as if you are listening for a distant sound or sounds. Way beyond the limits of ambient sound. Somewhere on the other side of the horizon. There is nothing to be heard, nothing in particular you are listening for, just be aware of sound in general. Sound that may be coming from somewhere far away. So it's the act of listening that relaxes you, not the hearing. Now, rest in that awareness.

Using your sense of hearing, keep directing your attention farther and farther afield. To the left and right, upwards and downwards, forwards and backwards. There's no hurry. You have all the time in the world to do this.

As you keep directing your attention outwards, you may become aware of individual sounds. Doesn't matter. Welcome them into your awareness, but pay them no

*attention. Allow them to be – neither trying to block them
out, nor evaluating them. You are simply directing your
attention outwards. In all directions. With a sense of being
right in the centre of it all.*

You can rest in this awareness.

By directing your attention so far afield, you expose your
senses to an almost infinite field of awareness – an indefinite,
structureless whole that contains all possible distractions.
By focusing on the general rather than the specific, minutia
such as individual feelings, discomforts, concepts, visuals, or
temperature changes become less intrusive than they would
normally be. By allowing room for these phenomena to exist,
you remove the element of surprise if, or rather *when*, they
work their way into your awareness.

STEP 3. CENTRING THE ATTENTION [⟶ INWARDS]

Two things have occurred. First, you centred your attention
in a physical place. Then, using your peripheral hearing, you
broadened it – that is, you widened your field of awareness so
that it accommodates all possible sensory phenomena (thus

reducing the chance of individual sounds, images, feelings, tastes, scents and physical sensations becoming distractions). With a subtle awareness of being in the centre of it all. The first step is physiological, the second psychological.

Although still using the sense of hearing, the next step takes the attention beyond the physiological and the psychological. You might recognise a well-known concentrative meditation technique here, which in this particular context is designed to bring your attention back to the core.

We're going to use a phenomenon that is familiar to you. So familiar, in fact, that when I suggest it to new meditators, they initially think there must be more to it. Something more sophisticated or esoteric. But we are keeping it as uncomplicated as possible.

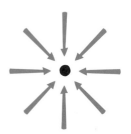

You are directing the attention to the breath. Or the sound of the breath. And in particular the sound of the *outbreath*. This is the part of the breathing cycle that involves no muscular effort. And when the breath is slow, this aligns with the calming part of the autonomic nervous system.

Your attention is wide, aware of the general rather than the specific, and you have a sense of being right in the centre of all. Now you can start bringing the attention back to the centre.

Slowly, progressively, allow yourself to become aware of the sound of your breathing. Perhaps this is not a sound you hear through the ears, so much as something that seems to emanate from deep inside. As if you are in the centre of the breathing. As if that sound is all around you. And as you withdraw your attention from the outside world, the sound of breathing fills your awareness.

This is the sound of breathing in general. Not 'my' breathing, just breathing. You are aware of the inflow, perhaps, but you are directing your attention to the sound of the outflow. Just the sound. Just the outbreath.

Nothing to do. Just keep directing your attention to that sound. And allow yourself to rest in the centre of the breathing experience.

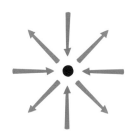

STEP 4. ONGOING
[OUTWARDS→ INWARDS]

The final step is the recognition that it is the *process* of directing the attention - outwards then inwards - that brings you peace, not what you direct your attention to. When the attention drifts outwards - which it does - you just redirect it back in to the sound. Back to the centre.

You are listening to the sound of the outbreath. That's all there is. When you find yourself thinking that there must be more to it than this, just direct your attention back to the sound.

When you notice that there are moments – seconds, minutes – when you are not aware of anything, or when you think you've finally got it, direct your attention back to the sound.

When you notice that you've become bored or listless or distracted, direct your attention back to the sound.

When you experience moments of elation, transcendence or profound contentedness, direct your attention back to the sound.

When the thought crosses your mind that this must be easier for some people than others, direct your attention back to the sound.

When you wonder how long you've been doing this, or what possible purpose could be served by continuing for another ten minutes, direct your attention back to the sound.

Then rest in this awareness.

This final step is not one to gloss over. It is the key to your ongoing enjoyment of becoming the master of directing your attention: the attention wanders outwards, you direct it inwards. It drifts out, you direct it back. Outwards, inwards, outwards, inwards.

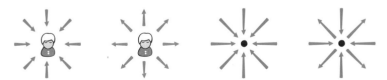

Now, before you go turning reflective on me, I want to clarify something: 'directing the attention inwards' does not mean introspection. Many people believe this is what meditation is about, but it's not. This meditation process has nothing to do with getting in touch with the 'inner you', or 'realising the Self', or any mysterious sounding things along those lines. It is just an exercise in training the attention. End of story.

Of course the outcome of meditation can be profound. But it is not meditation itself that is profound, it's how you experience the world in complete stillness.

THOSE FOUR STEPS IN PERSPECTIVE

You will appreciate how you can be two very different people from one day to the next, or even one hour to the next. For example, in the morning you're an uptight, chronically worried individual, fretting over how you're going to complete your work and pacify an irate customer at the same time . . . then by mid-afternoon, with the problem now solved, a bonus in your pocket, and the sun emerging from behind the clouds, you are a carefree soul with not a worry in the world. A massive shift. Generally it takes quite a while for

Mr Uptight to become Mr Chilled. But what if you could shorten this interval, and make the transformation more or less instantaneous?

Initially, everyone doubts they could do this. Even after reviewing all the promises of this book. Yet in one simple exercise, you can prove that it is possible.

Without doing another thing, direct your attention to where your body touches the floor or the chair. Bring all of your attention to this place. Then, just rest in this awareness a moment. [STEP 1]

As elementary as it seems, that step has important attributes. Above all, it enables you to succeed. You immediately feel that something is working. Moreover, it is a step anyone can master; you've probably done it countless times without even being aware of it. You are just directing your attention towards something familiar, the place where you make contact with the chair or floor. There is no particular significance in the action or the place; it's just a preparatory step like taking off your jacket and unrolling your mat before a yoga class.

Next, the change that is taking place is real. It can be demonstrated with fairly rudimentary laboratory equipment (although all we are concerned about is how it is demonstrated through your personal experience).

The shift of attention, away from the outside world to the place where you are now, begins a little chain reaction. Your metabolism is changing, your oxygen consumption decreasing, and your blood pressure, heartbeat and respiration rate are lowering. There are neurochemical changes taking place as well. What all this adds up to is you are starting to relax and feel even more at ease. And as long as you don't think about it, these changes continue.

The part of the change that can't be demonstrated with laboratory equipment is taking place on the inside. Only you are aware of it. The moment your attention is directed in the ways suggested in this book, all limitations dissolve. All doubts about whether a calming change can happen so quickly are forgotten. In this moment, everything becomes possible and your potential is unlimited.

It remains this way until you start thinking about it, in which case you're back to where you started.

Now you are feeling grounded in familiar territory, and your attention has shifted from 'out there' to here. Although you are still relying on the senses to some degree, you are moving right away from the physical. You are using one of the unfamiliar *peripheral* senses, in this case peripheral hearing. While it does register information, it does so in a broad, holistic way. So without being aware of anything in particular, you are starting to feel more reposeful, relaxed, at ease.

Why peripheral hearing rather than peripheral vision? Because in this case, hearing allows less opportunity for distraction.

Without focusing on anything in particular, start directing your attention outwards – stretching – farther and farther afield, as if you are listening for a distant sound or sounds. Nothing in particular, just sound in general. Employing your sense of hearing, just keep directing your attention farther and farther afield. To the left and right, upwards and downwards, forwards and backwards. [STEP 2]

Here's what has been happening. Step 1 takes you away from the busy, distracting, thought-filled outside world. What you are focusing on fills your attention. Where you make contact with the floor or the chair is all you are aware of. Before distractions come along you are moving on to Step 2. Step 1 directs the attention inwards, Step 2 directs it outwards.

Now that the Outwards→Inwards pattern has begun, Step 3 establishes the foundation for its continuation. You bring your attention back to what you might perceive as the attention centre.

Slowly, progressively, allow yourself to become aware of the sound of your breathing: a sound that seems to emanate from deep inside. Doesn't matter whether you can physically hear it or not, just be aware of the sound of the outbreath. Allow this to fill your awareness. [STEP 3]

Thereafter, the process – or Step 4 – is simply bringing the attention back to the sound of the outbreath. The attention will wander, and does so more consistently than you would choose. However, the training effect comes from recognising that it has wandered then re-directing it back to the outbreath. Over and over. Outwards → you notice → inwards. Simple as that.

Back to the centre

The limitations of everyday language are such that the Outwards→Inwards process sounds like you must direct your attention *towards* something.

However, as you find yourself becoming more familiar with the Outwards→Inwards process, the notion of 'me + what I am directing my attention towards' vanishes, and is replaced by an all-embracing awareness of being an integral part of the experience. It's like being in the epicentre of everything; what you are aware of is happening all around you – not in front, not behind, not above or to the sides – but all around.

In the forthcoming section, A Life Practice, you will see how this way of perceiving or experiencing can go much

 further than a seated meditation practice, and can be used to bring equanimity and clarity to your whole day. All determined by the one thing in life you have control over: where you direct the attention.

The more you practise those Outwards→Inwards shifts of attention, the more you are training the attention to rest in the present. And the easier you find being able to produce a state of restful attentiveness.

Just as with breathing itself, the process has no inherent meaning and no real completion point. Then one day you find it has become instinctive. Not because you will have mastered the ability to keep your attention permanently in the present (anyone who claims to be able to do this is exaggerating), but because you have the ability to rest your attention there when you need to.

And that's it. As elementary as this process may be, it is all you need to learn or master in concentrative meditation. When you strip away the historic overlays and attempts at adding meaning, virtually all practices turn out to be an elaboration on this.

Would you believe it's impossible to fail?

We could be sharing a first here. You could be reading the first instruction book ever written where it's impossible for the user to fail – providing you follow the steps. However, on the way to this discovery there are some minor belief impediments for you to cast aside.

The initial one relates to cause and effect. You've spent your entire life believing that specific actions result in specific outcomes. You smile at strangers, they smile back; you lift weights, you build muscle; you learn Spanish phrases, and one day you will converse in Spanish. What you learn from this is to start with an outcome in mind, then to work back. I want strangers to like me, so I smile at them first; I want muscles, so I lift weights; I want to be able to converse in Spanish, so I study one phrase at a time. Now you're reading that this meditation approach is different: that the *process* is what we focus on, and the outcome is irrelevant.

How can this be? Haven't we already established that the process in this book is intended to train the attention? Isn't this an outcome? Why wouldn't we start out with this in mind?

Because our interest is in the present. The present cannot be experienced while you are focused on the future. And even though training the attention will be a by-product of the process, you need to be open to the beauty and satisfaction within the process itself.

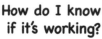

How do I know if it's working?

Another belief to cast aside is that there is some way of measuring the Outwards→Inwards process. This belief can manifest in a number of ways: thinking that other people are better at it than you, that you're not the type, that you get more distracted than others do, that there is a right way and wrong way of doing it, that there are good meditators and poor meditators, or that there are stages of development you can benchmark yourself against.

You probably recognise the paradox by now: if you try to evaluate or compare an experience of the present you are not experiencing it. Or are no longer experiencing it. The only time you can compare something is after it has occurred – where you can weigh it up against some other experience from your past. Bottom line: you cannot experience the present at the same time as you are focused on what has already happened.

The final belief to cast aside is that the Outwards→Inwards approach involves effort or some degree of challenge. You often hear things like, 'I'm no good at this meditation thing, my mind keeps wandering.' Or, 'I've been practising for months now and still my thoughts are all over the place.'

Sometimes the most obvious discoveries are the hardest to see. The surest way to prove that no effort or difficulty is involved is to put the Outwards→Inwards process to the test. Then, if you experience any difficulty you will know that you are using methodology other than what I've described. When you use the practice described on these pages, without expectation, the difficulty vanishes. There will be times when other factors bring discomfort and baggage - such as illness, physical conditions or even pre-existing emotional states - but the Outwards→Inwards process itself is effortless.

If you find it difficult to concentrate or to keep bringing your attention back, it's because you are trying. Give up on trying; you are not meant to try. If you think this is not working properly for you, it's because you think there's a right way and a wrong way of doing it. And this is not the case.

The nature of attention is that it wanders. With training it will become more stable, for sure, but it will still wander. If it didn't, you're probably in a coma.

The beauty of the Outwards→Inwards approach is that distraction and losing the plot are key parts of the process. If there is no distraction, there is no process. You begin with a state of restful attentiveness, then when the attention wanders outwards, which it will, you direct it back. Whether it takes you five seconds to notice the drift or half an hour makes no difference; *it is the becoming aware of the distraction, then directing the attention back that is the process.* What you may initially consider to be the weakness – the straying, the fidgetting, the distractions, the wandering thoughts, the insights, the forgetting-why-I'm-doing-this – is not a weakness at all. It is an integral part of the process.

For this very reason, there is no such thing as a good meditator or a bad meditator.

True, there are long-term meditators and there are novices, but even here the only difference is that long-term meditators are familiar with the wandering and recognise it as part of the process, while the novices think the wandering is some kind of failing.

The most experienced meditator still experiences a drifting attention. Even after 50 years of practice. Even if they removed themselves from worldly distractions, and dedicated their lives to meditating in a poorly heated hermitage in the most remote part of Nepal. When they sat down to meditate they would still forget what their intention was or what they were focusing on, they would still be distracted by subtle noises and discomforts, they would still note temperature changes and find themselves planning what they're going to do when the sun came out. This is the way it goes. It is not a failing; it is the process.

There will be occasions when it is all so subtle and streamlined that you think you've spent the last half hour doing nothing. Other times, half an hour has passed and you think you've spent the whole time wondering about your credit card bill. One is not superior to the other. It is just a process, an exercise in directing the attention.

The moment you recognise that distraction exists and then direct your attention back to the sound of your breath, you have a meditation practice. The more you notice such things, the more you strengthen it. The principle is the same as the athlete using barbells - it is the resistance of the weights that builds strength, not the act of lifting. It is the recognition of distraction then the turning back that trains the attention, not the avoidance of distraction in the first place.

For those reasons alone you cannot fail with this Outwards→Inwards process. You may be tempted to perceive them as failures, but distractions are a critical part of the game. For you. For everyone.

When you leave the chair

The steps described so far are designed to train the attention through a simple seated practice.

There are many worldly benefits that flow from this – more stable emotions, clarity of mind, strengthened immune system, improved health and wellbeing, and so on – but these are by-products. Our primary focus is on improving the ability to keep the attention in the present.

An even greater reward comes later, when you can take this new found ability out into the world with you. To be able to apply it in your work, in your relationships, in your sporting activities, when you're eating and resting, when you are facing crises, when you're having fun and when you're bored. Imagine how rich life will be when – from an underlying state of restful attentiveness – you can bring moment-to-moment awareness to all aspects of it, acutely aware of all that is happening as it is happening, experiencing the full sweep of existence wholeheartedly. With all of your attention.

The steps that facilitate this are slightly different to those we have covered, but the Outwards→Inwards principle remains the same.

Before we move on to that, however, there's another issue you're probably going to have to deal with. *Where are you going to find the time to practise this?*

Making it
permanent

Pause here

In this section, you're going to discover how to make the skills we've been talking about a permanent feature of your life.

You know from past experience that it doesn't matter how enthusiastic you are about making changes, or how skilful or motivating your course or teacher might be, the determination seems to fade very quickly. Relapsing often takes only days or weeks. This tendency explains why weight-loss diets have high failure rates, and why home gyms and exercise machines never wear out.

In all the years I've been teaching and writing about meditation and related fields, I have wondered why some people succeed with their long-term endeavours, while others become serial restarters. There is a pattern. And it seems to have less to do with motivation than it does with finding space for the practices to flourish.

Good intentions get you some of the way and powerful motivation will take you further, but they are no match for the mix of work pressures, family commitments, non-stop communications and wall-to-wall titillation that overwhelm your day. With so many distractions and competing interests at play, you need more than motivation. You need space to be able to put it to work. The place you're going to find it is more accessible than you would think.

Pause for a moment. Cast your mind back a few decades. Once upon a time, there were gaps in your life. Spaces. Time to look out the window, play with your toys, fantasise, go on neighbourhood adventures with your dog. Now cast your imagination back even further, to another less complicated age, maybe even before your parents' time. Then, there was time (space) to cook up a soup stock, to write a letter, to read a book with long paragraphs, to wash dishes by hand, to add up rows of numbers without the aid of a calculator and to go on Sunday afternoon strolls.

Why is it that today, with all our pre-packaged products and time-saving devices, we find ourselves too busy to contemplate taking on anything new? How did we go from having space in our lives to having an endless series of over-lapping demands?

There is a way you can re-introduce some of that space. It doesn't require great willpower or exertion. It involves the creation of a little space-making habit. A barely-noticeable habit that takes up none of your precious time, and doesn't add to your burden of things you feel you have to do.

It's time to pause again. Turn your mind to an average day in your life. When you analyse what it consists of, you'll end up with a list of discrete events. All separate. In your mind breakfast (event A) is quite separate from your ride to work (event B), and that is quite separate from the mid-morning meeting with your boss (event C), and so on.

Well that's how it seems when you think about it. But when you're in the thick of the action, it seems nothing like that – especially during a working day.

The separation between events is no longer there. You're planning your day as you put on your eyeliner, you're reading the sales report as you walk from the car park, you're answering yesterday's email on your smartphone as you wait for your boss to turn up for the meeting. All these theoretically discrete events have become one wall-to-wall activity. What's more, the busier you believe yourself to be, or the more pressure you feel you're under, the more those events and responsibilities seem to overlap.

There are two ways out of this dilemma: either rearrange the events, or change the way you think about them. You can rule out the first one, because you already know that doesn't work. So is it possible to change the way you think? If there was some means of suddenly switching your outlook – one moment seeing the responsibility-crammed day of an adult, the next moment seeing the wide-open day you enjoyed as a child – the pressure would be off. You would have more space in your day.

Maybe you can pull that off by applying reason. Try this: if you compare your typical day with that of your great-great-grandparents, you will conclude that there is no material difference: 24 hours, less eight for sleep, a couple for eating, one for travel (slower transport then meant similar travel hours), and the remainder is where you think the problems are. You protest that the issue is not so much the number of hours as what you have to accomplish within them – made all the more difficult by challenging child-minding arrangements, public transport timetables and occupational demands. Then you recall hearing about how your great-great-grandmother had to light the fire each morning, cook breakfast for seven children, boil water on the stove top, wash clothes in the back yard (by hand), before walking into town for her job in the haberdashery store.

Did that comparison take any of the pressure off? Of course it didn't. Rather than go through more comparisons, why don't we just accept that reason alone won't produce the feeling or perception of having space in your day. So, if we've ruled out rearranging events, relying solely on reason, what other alternatives exist?

Accept that attitude plays as an important a role as your clock or your calendar, and you're on the way to making space in your life. Accept that two people can respond differently to exactly the same pressures – one person thrives while the other merely endures – and you're on the way to finding the underlying calm and equanimity that this book is about.

Finding more space in your day is a straightforward matter of adjusting perceptions. Once you do that, and then make a habit out of it, you've solved the problem.

Most people who feel pressured by modern life share the same mental trait: most of their day is spent projecting and reflecting. They are thinking about what they didn't get to cover in the previous meeting at the same time as they are preparing their charts for the meeting later in the day. Or they are thinking about what they're going to cook for dinner tonight at the same time as they are answering their emails. Habitually thinking about what happened before or what's going to happen later, with their attention constantly moving between past and future. You know what that's a recipe for.

You also know there is a better way. Although it's less common than the past-future model, it is far more calming. Not only does it produce the state of restful attentiveness I've been writing about, it creates the impression of having unlimited time and space in your life! And all you have to do to enjoy this is to decide where your attention is directed:

instead of compulsively moving it from the past to the future, you direct it to the present.

We now have an Outwards→Inwards process that enables you to direct your attention to the present for 20–30 minutes, maybe once or twice a day. Is that enough? What about the rest of your day? Wouldn't you like to be able to do something with your attention at other times of the day?

As familiar as they may be with the principle of focusing on the present, few people have a practical application for it. Here's an easy one. Instead of trying to avoid the past or the future, instead of trying to work out where or what the present is, you direct the attention to a very familiar part of everyday life. Not this thing or that thing, or this event or that event, but the space *between* events. As momentary as that space may be, you can use it as a place of letting go and re-grouping. Of restoration. Of finding stillness and balance.

Pause again

You may have noticed how the more pressure you're under, the more pressure you seem to create for yourself. When you're hemmed in by deadlines and mountains of work, for some illogical reason all you can see are the other things you have to do. The desk needs tidying. The loose hem on your skirt needs fixing. The phone bill needs to be paid. The door handle is hanging at a strange angle. Things that you never noticed when you were feeling relaxed are suddenly front of mind. Yet they all disappear when you do one thing.

Pause.

Take a moment to let go of everything that relates to the outside world, to step back from the chaos, and to bring all of your attention to this little space that has cropped up between the last thing you were doing and the next thing you have to do.

Bring your attention to this space and you are suddenly feeling grounded and at ease. You're in the centre of everything that's going on. The world seems slightly more orderly. Outside stuff no longer seems quite so important. As for the pressure – well that's on pause. The workload hasn't reduced, deadlines haven't moved, they just don't seem menacing any more. And in this space you have the room to really let go of all this pressure and just relax . . . knowing that when you do return to the fray you will be bringing a broader, more orderly and more effective perspective.

A pause is all it takes.

Pause.

Stop what you are doing and direct your attention to the present. Pause between one work activity and the next, and allow yourself to settle. And again as you stand in the queue at the coffee shop. And as you wait for your computer to restart. And as you wait for the tea to draw or the pasta to cook. Pause before you open your next email. Pause before cleaning your teeth and going to bed.

A pause enables you to top up, or restore, that state of restful attentiveness that you enjoyed in your morning meditation. If you need a more down-to-earth rationale than that, think

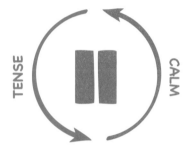

of it as a mini-reset of the tense–calm cycle that we've been speaking about. (I have no idea whether it literally reverses the cycle, but it sure is a positive step towards pre-venting it spinning out of control.)

Even though you could do this anywhere, anytime, the best way to create this pause habit is to concentrate on the space between one activity and another. You'll find this easy to remember because it falls at the end or beginning of things that already feature in your awareness.

Make it even easier on yourself by nominating an activity that occurs many times a day. One executive I know pauses as he waits for the elevator to arrive at his floor. As he has to move between three different levels several times a day, he finds dozens of pause opportunities without having to make a single decision. There will be similar meaningless activities that happen recurrently throughout your day. If you can think of one right now, make a note of it. You can put it to use when you get to the end of this chapter.

How long should a pause be for it to become effective? Ten seconds? A minute? Longer? Refer back to the first step of the Outwards→Inwards process. This is the step that grounds the exercise in an accessible place, and helps you to move your attention from 'somewhere out there' to 'here'.

Just direct your attention to where your body meets the floor or the ground or the chair. Nothing else to do or think about. Just direct your attention here, and allow yourself to feel anchored in this place. Even though the body will be relaxing and thoughts slowing down, all you need to focus on is this place where you are now.

How long did that take? Twenty seconds? A minute? It was effective from the moment it began. But as the habit becomes more ingrained, you will find it's like drawing a breath – something you just do, without consideration and without any concept of the duration.

However, I know you won't rest until you have a figure. If you apply your mathematical brain to my suggestions above, you will conclude that X number of pauses, each of around Y minutes, add up to XY minutes out of your already busy day. How can you afford that?

Our pauses don't work that way. They actually increase your efficiency and presence of mind, so you end up feeling you have more time to play with, not less.

Real long-lasting change comes from *making a habit* out of the occasional pauses. That means many times a day. The more you do it, the more intuitive and habitual it becomes. Then one day you will find yourself pausing instinctively, which means the ongoing peacefulness I've been promising you is at hand.

Linking the pauses

A pause instantly centres you. And reminds you how easy it is to feel settled and calm, even for only a few seconds at a time. Because pauses meld into your routine almost invisibly, and demand no planning or effort, you may find yourself fitting more and more of them into your day. This accelerates the building of a habit. And introduces a lot of space and restoration opportunities.

The ever-present reminder

Walk out into the street now and you will see many people doing exactly the same thing. They'll also be doing it at work, in the library, at the bus stop and in the supermarket: playing with the smartphone.

This device compels you to glance at it many times a day. What if every time you did that you received a little signal to pause? You could transform a phone-watching habit into a powerful pause reminder. Dozens of opportunities to stop what you are doing and direct your attention to the present.

Go to my website and you'll find a screensaver that will remind you to pause every time you pick up your phone. Not very technologically advanced, but effective. And no charge. You'll find it at: www.calmcentre.com/pause.

When you think back to the premise at beginning of this book – an underlying peacefulness that you can rely on for the rest of your life – you may think this would require more than just slipping a few pauses into your routine. And it will. But not much more. In fact, it is achieved by just linking a range of important, stillness-creating opportunities.

The first is where you establish the benchmark for your day: a seated (or reclining or walking) meditation such as we have already experimented with. First thing in the morning is good, but you can do it any time you choose. Millions of people believe a practice like this is all you ever need to achieve what this book is about. It does take a little more, but not much.

The second opportunity is when you add a range of pauses to your day. No need to think this through, just take a few seconds to settle in the space between one activity and the next. Remember to do it many times a day, even if only for a few seconds.

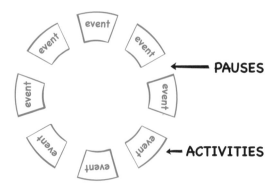

No effort is involved here. Just by adding those two opportunities together – the formal practice and the pauses – you greatly reduce the time it takes to build a foundation of equanimity.

The third part of the equation accelerates and intensifies this.

It occurs when you use your day-to-day activities – work, eating and drinking, chores, conversations, relationships, even dealing with problems – as a way of keeping your attention in the present. We will address the mechanics of this in the next part, A Life Practice.

Creating a habit

Teachers, trainers and authors can get very glib about the business of creating positive habits, and are prone to pointing out just how little effort and motivation is required. You'd have to be pretty gullible to believe some of what is claimed, but let's examine what is possible.

To begin with, the mere act of pausing and focusing on the present, even for only a few seconds, will help you feel calm, centred and on top of things. One follows the other. Automatically.

You can easily prove this for yourself. The more often you do this – pause and bring your attention to the present – the deeper and more ingrained the habit becomes. Once again, this is something you can easily prove for yourself. This brings us to the wait-and-see part of the story.

When you have paused this way a sufficient number of times you reach the stage where the underlying stillness is always there. It becomes a central part of your awareness.

You may wonder what sort of time frame this involves. Fast-talking salesmen have trained us to expect unbelievable results in unbelievably brief times. 'Develop rock hard abs in just two minutes a day.' 'Lose ten kilos in a week.' 'Become a millionaire in six months.' Loose claims like these are often supported by myths that relate to habit formation. Such as: if you repeat a particular activity for 21 (or 22, 28, 29 or 66, depending on the source) consecutive days, you form a habit. Or if you repeat a physical action 100 times (or 300, 5000 or 66,000 times), you create muscle memory. Myths and partial truths.

Fortunately there are some reliable statistical studies that have been conducted in the area of habit formation. Here is a quick summary of some that relate to our topic.

- Habits are formed in an average of 66 days. Note the word 'average'. Simple and enjoyable habits can be formed in a few days, while complex or less desirable ones take longer.

- New motor patterns can be created within 300 to 500 repetitions of a certain action. (Take care because it can take ten times as many repetitions to correct it!)
- You can reshape an ingrained mental image in around three weeks. That means it takes about 21 days for your new house to seem like home, or for your newly shaped nose to seem like it belongs on your face.

repetition
repetition
repetition
repetition
repetition
repetition
repetition
repetition
repetition
repetition
repetition
repetition
repetition
repetition

It's not my intention to explore these findings in any depth other than to point out the obvious: if you repeat an action for a couple of months it becomes a habit; if what you are doing involves a pleasant experience the habit forms faster; if a physical action is required it takes at least 300 repetitions before it is ingrained; and if you want to change a mental image of yourself – for example, seeing yourself as a calm person rather than a tense one – work on it for three weeks.

A positive habit with immediate gratification

The general nature of habit formation is commonsense. Whether you call it repetition or practice the results come from doing the same thing over and over until it sticks.

You might wonder, then, why we find it so hard to persist with a desirable practice such as meditation, even when we know it leads to a habit we would love to have. Intellectually, we can accept that it is desirable. Experience confirms that no effort is required. So what's the problem? It relates to pleasure.

Let's try a thought experiment. Think about carrots. Crisp, juicy, fresh-from-the-garden carrots. Close your eyes, and bring one to mind. Use all of your senses: smell, taste, feel. Feel the firm texture. The coolness. Imagine what that carrot would taste like.

Now, if you were to have one of those carrots delivered to your plate every day, how long do you think it would be until you had developed a carrot-eating habit? *How many months was that?*

Now turn your imagination to chocolate. Doesn't matter exactly what type of chocolate, or how fattening or expensive it might be. As this is only happening in your imagination you can really let yourself go. Close your eyes, and bring chocolate to mind. Use all of your senses. Smell, taste, feel. Be aware of the texture. Feel the sensuous way it melts at body temperature. Now for the big one . . . can you taste it?

If someone were to deliver a block of that chocolate to your plate every day, how long do you think it would be before you developed a chocolate-eating habit? *Really? Only a week?*

It's a bit unfair the way nature structures these things, but the positive activities of life (maintaining a healthy diet, keeping fit, learning a new language, being considerate of others and so on) are seldom as immediately enticing as the less positive ones (eating chocolate, lazing around, taking care of your own needs first). And in terms of habit formation, the naughty ones seem to do the trick much faster than the wholesome ones.

If our goal is to create a calm habit in the shortest possible time, maybe we should acknowledge this and factor in some 'naughty' qualities like pleasure, novelty and the promise of instant gratification.

Turn your imagination to this. Tomorrow morning, not long after the sun comes up, something miraculous takes place. You roll out of bed, perhaps have a cup of tea, then just sit around and allow it to happen. All your responsibilities and workloads disappear. All those things you thought you had to do have been postponed indefinitely. Then, with no effort on your part, you get to experience 20–30 minutes of absolute peacefulness. It just washes over you. All your cares and worries – if they ever existed – wash away with

pleasure
pleasure
pleasure
pleasure
pleasure
pleasure
pleasure
pleasure
pleasure
pleasure
pleasure

it. You drift, floating, carefree, complete. Everything in order, and everything perfect in its own way. Not a hint of any regrets, fears, responsibilities, deadlines or worldly pressure. Amazing.

Then the day after tomorrow it happens again. And the morning after that. And the next. Maybe it also happens in the evenings before you get ready for bed. Twenty to 30 minutes of pure peacefulness.

By any measure, those are pleasurable moments. They make you feel good. But unlike with other pleasures, the satisfaction continues. You can imagine how routinely indulging in an enjoyable activity like that might become habitual.

repetition + pleasure = habit

Now that we know there's a formula for habit formation, it would be helpful if there was one for commitment building as well. Commitment is the act of dedicating yourself to a particular course of action, and has two requirements: motivation and a plan of action.

The motivation part should be easy. Experiment with the Outwards→Inwards process a few times and see if you feel better as a result.

If you need more reasons, check out the range of physical, emotional and spiritual benefits that flow from a meditation practice. There's no point in trying to list them all here as an internet search will highlight a wealth of published material.

Makes me feel good!

equanimity
peace of mind

wisdom   clarity

stress   feeling of
relief   wholeness

better   stable
sleep   emotions

lower
cholesterol

The benefits they write about range from the mundane ('I sleep better'), to the less tangible ('it produces beneficial changes at a cellular or even genetic level'), to the profound ('I experience a sense of Oneness'). Any one or combination of these could provide the motivation you're looking for.

Once you have the motivation, you need a plan of action. You know what to do. Start rising 20 minutes earlier tomorrow. Don't think about whether you can spare the time (you can) or how to make it perfect (irrelevant), just put aside 20 minutes as a pre-breakfast, pre-getting-ready-for-work time for enjoying the Outwards→Inwards process. Commit to doing it every morning until you feel the habit taking over. Oh yes, if you're thinking that it might suit you better to do it in the evening, or both morning and evening, go for it!

Want another suggestion? Pause now . . . and ask yourself this question: can I begin this routine tomorrow?

Not exciting, but far from boring

There is one more detail to address before we take your practice into the wider world. It's to do with a challenge that some meditators face after the novelty has worn off their practice. It relates to boredom and impatience.

Seated meditation is usually 20-30 minutes where nothing much happens. This contrasts with most activities in life where something either happens or is meant to happen. One of the most frequent complaints I hear from new meditators is, 'I sat there for half an hour, did all the things you said, but nothing happened' - as if that represented some sort of failure on one of our parts. Even experienced meditators voice this sentiment sometimes. How easily we forget that the central premise of meditation is that *nothing is meant to happen.*

However, modern human nature being what it is, we tend to think that if we do something, something else should happen as a result. Simultaneously, we have been trained to expect life to be endlessly stimulating, which leads us to view the *absence* of stimulation as being less than ideal. There is only restlessness in such illusions. If nothing is happening or if there is no stimulation, then boredom and impatience can arise.

Although boredom is familiar to all of us, it is not well understood. One thing we're certain of: it's never our fault, because there is always someone else or some situation we can blame. However, if we recognised what was really behind it, it could be avoided. For example, boredom only arises when your mind is active, and when you think you have things to do but feel constrained (such as trapped in a non-engaging activity). Yet boredom seldom arises when you are chilled, with low arousal and your attention at rest.

An active mind without action is a recipe for boredom.

An chilled mind without action means boredom is unlikely.

Can you see how this relates to meditation?

Now turn your attention to impatience. Just like boredom, impatience requires an active, energetic mind. But it also requires something else – for you to expect something to happen. Expectation is not a topic you think about a lot; if pressed you'd probably say it meant just having a belief about the future. It can be more insidious than that. Usually it involves having an emotional attachment to an outcome, maybe with an unconscious urge to find or establish order. For example, you give someone a bunch of flowers, you expect them to be grateful as a result. If they thank you, everything is in order. But if they don't, you experience disappointment, hurt, misunderstanding or resentment.

An active mind with a level of expectation is a recipe for boredom.

Yet a chilled mind with no expectation means boredom is unlikely.

Can you see how this relates to meditation?

Boredom and impatience cannot exist when the attention is in the present. Here you are content just to be. You feel no urge to manage how the meditation should occur. You have no expectations as to how it should be working for you. And you are wholly focused on the moment you are experiencing.

A life practice

You're almost there

By now you may have experienced how the state of restful attentiveness in your morning meditation sets the tone for your day. And you may have experimented with topping that up, or restoring it, with brief pauses throughout the day.

Things go well for a while, then plateau. The novelty of a new meditation practice eventually wears off, personal circumstances change, you forget about those pauses (before the habit has been ingrained), and dramas arise from the most obscure places, always putting your newfound equilibrium to the test.

Then you recall a claim from earlier in the book, that *ongoing* inner stillness requires an additional step. This is when you apply your new way of directing the attention to the whole of your life.

There are short-term and long-term benefits to this. The short-term ones become more noticeable as the process becomes more familiar. In summary, it makes life richer and more rewarding. Food tastes better, your relationships seem deeper, your work is more satisfying, your play is more enjoyable, and your skills seem more integrated. As for the drawbacks of life, not only do they seem less threatening, but their ability to cause suffering has been reduced.

Longer term is where the big changes await. We're talking nothing less than a profound shift in awareness. This is the foundation of equanimity I've been writing about. Perhaps those words don't scream out the way some of my other more worldly descriptions do, but I promise that when you experience this everything falls into place. With no fears, regrets or doubts to cloud your vision, there is pristine clarity. Not the sort that enables you to explain things or even understand things, but the deep, unshakeable certainty that everything is in order, everything is okay.

There are two mutually supporting phases that bring you to this point. The first is training the attention to be able to rest in the present. The second is applying that ability to the whole of your life. (In essence, these phases are the same: you are training the attention while you apply it to the whole of your life.)

Central to all of that is a simple practice. You take the one aspect of life that you have total control over, choosing where you direct your attention, and make a habit out of directing it to the present. We've described the process behind this as Outwards→Inwards.

You use this process in your regular seated meditation. Throughout the day you apply it to a variety of little pause opportunities, possibly focusing on the space between one activity and the next. (This adds to, refreshes or restores the peacefulness you started the day with.)

Then to complete the picture, you use the same process to bring all of your attention to whatever activity you are involved in during the day. Perhaps focusing on one activity per day in the beginning, then adding more as the process becomes more familiar.

The whole-of-life practice

Our focus now is turning Outwards→Inwards into a dawn to dusk, equanimity-building practice.

We began the day in a seated meditation context.

Just direct the attention inwards. Focus on where you are now. Allow the body to relax, feel yourself centred here.

As you feel your weight anchoring you to the floor or the seat, start to broaden the attention outwards. So that, gradually, it encompasses the whole field of your awareness. Take your time.

When the entire field is in your awareness, bring the attention inwards again, back to the centre. Listen for the subtle sound of the outbreath. As if the sound is all around you.

Stay with that sound. When your attention wanders outwards, just bring it back to the centre, back to this one thing, the sound of your breath. The attention wanders outwards, you keep bringing it back to the centre. Outwards, back to the centre. Outwards→Inwards. That's the whole story.

From a classical viewpoint, those steps describe a form of concentrative meditation, where you focus on one thing until the mind becomes 'single-pointed'. Following the classic line there is another type of practice that some say is an alternative, others say is an essential part of a complete awareness-enhancing practice, and others (like me) say is just a variation on the same. This is known by many names, but is commonly referred to as mindfulness. Sometimes it's treated as a formal practice, but we're going to treat it as just a practical way of applying the attention.

Before we head too far down this path it's worth challenging what is understood by this word, mindfulness, and its more slogan-like alternatives such as 'being in the moment'. Mostly people speak about it as something you do, like strengthening your core muscles or avoiding carbs. Or something to squeeze in a busy day along with Pilates, tennis and tummy crunches.

It wasn't always this way. The initial interest in the topic stemmed from traditional Buddhist teaching, particularly as it was introduced to the West in the late fifties to early sixties. My exposure to it came from the Theravada school, who viewed it a little differently to other Buddhist schools. They taught it as a bread-and-butter approach to experiencing life as it is, rather than how one might imagine it to be. Although not presented to me as such, mindfulness was more of an easy-to-implement approach to life than a deep philosophy.

Not everyone sees it that way, of course. It never ceases to amaze me how the simplest practices can become complicated when experts get involved. I remember being asked to address a series of mindfulness conferences a few years ago. In the main, these were attended by academics, spiritual teachers and practitioners, and many psychologists – people you would consider to be 'in the know'. Yet the contrasts and contradictions in viewpoints was extraordinary.

Perhaps we shouldn't be surprised. You only have to do a web search of 'mindfulness' to find endless interpretations and appropriations. It seems to be a topic where anyone can speak with authority – personal trainers, life coaches, yoga teachers, journalists, and practically everyone who has ever opened a text book on psychology – yet there is very little commonality about what the practice is.

Further complicating the above is the paradox that it takes mindful behaviour to recognise mindfulness or the lack thereof. Harvard Professor of Psychology, Ellen Langer, expressed this beautifully in a radio interview: 'When you're mindless, you're not there to know you're not there.'

The only reason I draw your attention to this diversity is so that it doesn't become a point of confusion for what's ahead. What we're about to explore encompasses all of the clichés: being present, being in the moment, experiencing the now, flow, mindfulness or whatever you like to call it. You will find this is the key to (a) maintaining a sense of inner calm and equanimity as you ride the ups and downs of everyday life, (b) quickly recovering your inner calm and equanimity when those ups and downs throw you off balance, and (c) experiencing everyday life with a completeness you seldom experience.

The process that follows is intrinsically simple. It dovetails with the Outwards→Inwards approach we covered earlier. It does this in an uncomplicated and effortless way. And it all flows naturally when you have a sense of directing your attention from what we metaphorically describe as 'the centre'.

Direct from the centre

You direct the attention inwards, then outwards, then inwards again when it wanders. If you apply everyday logic to this, you might conclude that this all about directing your attention somewhere. Or some place.

However, after the first few times of using the Outwards→Inwards process, you forget about what or where you are directing your attention to because the sense of 'me plus something else' is no longer there. From that moment your interest is only where you direct the attention *from*.

This doesn't mean directing it from a physical place such as your brain, your heart, or some other part of your anatomy or being. Nor does it mean that this is something you sense (which would imply that it is physical), or something you understand (which would imply it is conceptual or intellectual). It's more subtle than that.

The best way I can describe this is as being wholly within the experience. Here there is no room for analysis or evaluation, only what is happening. If you're having a conversation, there is only conversation. If you're making love, there is only making love. If you're skiing, there is only skiing. If you're eating an orange, there is only eating. There are *not* two separate parts to this, me and my experience, there is only the experience. Moreover the experience is not in front of you, or below you, or above you, or behind you; it's as if you are part of the experience. A central part.

This subtle awareness is familiar to long-term meditators, but words get in the way when they try to describe it to others. Even referring to it as an experience is clumsy, because that suggests some sort of beginning and end, some sort of separateness from other experiences. Whereas your awareness is of the continuity, of the flow, of the equanimity that underpins – or *can* underpin – everything.

I've made it sound exotic, haven't I? Yet, if ever there was an opposite to exotic, this is it. So simple, natural and uncomplicated. So everyday.

The centre of ongoing calm

The Outwards→Inwards process I described may seem like a structured meditation practice. It is – but only in the sense that it is designed to take place in a regular form on a regular basis. At least once a day is the ideal, more often is even better. The more you do it, and the less you think about it, the more intuitive it becomes. You will notice the act of bringing the attention back to the centre (that is, allowing the attention to rest in the present) becoming more habitual. And as long as you don't apply effort, this habit will form faster than you imagine.

Sooner or later a thought pops into your head: 'Hey, I'd like to be able to extend this feeling into the rest of my day.'

If you've practised the Outwards→Inwards process in a regular seated practice, even if only a few times, you're ready to take the ultimate step of spreading it throughout your day.

The good part about this is there's nothing new to learn; you already know all you need to. The same methodology applies. It's all about where you direct your attention.

If there is a difference between the structured practice and this, it is purely a matter of where and when you do it. Previously, we talked about a 20- or 30-minute seated session – ostensibly away from the active, day-to-day world – and now we're going to take it into that day-to-day world with no time constraints at all.

There are no limits to where this can be practised. Do it when you're adding up figures, when you're cooking, when you're on the bus, when you're mowing the lawn, when you're under pressure, when you're talking to your friends, when you're giving a presentation or a speech. Do it when you pause. Do it when you're meditating. In the beginning, when you consciously use the Outwards→Inwards process in a limited range of activities, a little forethought or scheduling may be necessary. Eventually, though, it becomes intuitive. Then you find yourself doing it at all sorts of times and places, without objectives, and without expecting anything in return. This is an illuminating stage.

We're going to focus on the first phase of an ongoing process of integrating the Outwards→Inwards habit into all parts of your life. I will outline the steps, then explain how to weave them into your day.

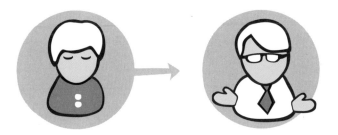

To begin with, choose an activity that doesn't require a lot of thinking – washing the car, raking the leaves, preparing and drinking a cup of tea, going for a walk in the park. Exactly the same principles apply to more complex activities, but we'll start with something relatively mechanical. Say, for example, the activity is taking a walk in the park.

Pause for a moment. Commit to performing this particular action with *all* of your attention. Yes, all of it. No half measures.

STEP 1. WHERE AM I NOW? [⟶ INWARDS]

Direct your attention to where you make physical contact with the path. Bring all of your attention here, and allow yourself to feel centred and grounded in this place. Spend as long as you like on this step, even though the change begins after only a few seconds. Now rest in the centre of that awareness.

STEP 2. WIDENING THE ATTENTION [OUTWARDS→]

When you are feeling relaxed, spend 20 seconds or so directing the attention outwards. In all directions. Use one of your peripheral senses to broaden the field of awareness – either your peripheral vision (taking in more visual information around you without moving your eyes) or your peripheral hearing (listening for sound way off in the distance). Keep directing the attention outwards – left, right, upwards, downwards, forwards, backwards – simultaneously. Spend as long as you like on this step, then just rest in the centre of that awareness.

STEP 3. CENTRING THE ATTENTION [→ INWARDS]

Maybe less than a minute or so has passed until this point. Those first two steps were designed to change the nature of your attention from 'scattered' to 'focused'. Now it is time to bring all of your attention to the activity at hand.

Where in the early part of this book Step 3 had you focusing on the sound of the breath, this time it is focusing on an everyday activity: walking in the park. If you direct your attention from *within* the experience or activity, there will only be room in your awareness for that.

 *Start bringing the attention back to the activity at hand. Be aware of it being directed from within the heart of the experience. Be aware of the complete act of walking. Not 'me' doing the walking, not walking as some kind of activity that 'I' am involved in, just walking. There's a deeply satisfying, even restful place in the centre of this.*

STEP 4. ONGOING [OUTWARDS⟶ INWARDS]

On paper, the art of walking mindfully is dead simple: you purposely place one foot in front of the other, doing it to the best of your ability, while you maintain a broad awareness of what's around you, without being distracted by any particular element of it.

That may be easy to do for a minute or so, but is more challenging to maintain.

Unless . . .

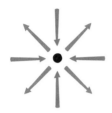

There is only the walking. The walking is everything. When you think that doesn't make sense, or there must be more to the process than this, direct your attention back to the walking. When you find yourself realising that there are moments – seconds, minutes – when you are not aware of anything else, or when you think you've finally 'got it', direct your attention back to the walking. When you find yourself realising that you've become bored or listless or distracted, direct your attention back to the walking. When the thought crosses your mind that this must be easier for some people than others, direct your attention back to the walking. When you wonder how long you've been doing this, or what possible purpose could be served by it, direct your attention back to the walking.

Your attention drifts out, you direct it back. It drifts out, you direct it back. Outwards, inwards, outwards, inwards.

In the early stages, try that Outwards→Inwards process on a variety of chores and activities. Choose any activity that you would normally do, and approach it with all of your attention. Only for a minute or so. Several times a day. This is all part of the habit-build. In time you will discover it has become a more efficient and far more rewarding way of doing what you regularly do.

The same steps in all activities

 It's not all that difficult to see how the Outwards→Inwards process might apply to a repetitive and mentally undemanding activity such as walking in the park. Or like eating a meal, nursing a baby to sleep, doing Warrior Two at yoga, filing documents, listening to music, taking public transport, running on the treadmill, or doing the dishes. But what about the more demanding activities that you encounter in the workplace? Doesn't focusing on a single activity, with all of your attention, seem like a less efficient way to work? Wouldn't you be inclined to think that, when working, it would be important to be continually thinking ahead and reviewing where you've been?

These are popular views, but are based on a fallacy about focusing and multi-tasking. Despite the heroic assumptions of some in the workplace, no one can multi-task. A normal human brain is not up to the task. It can focus on only one thing at a time. (You can be aware of many things, but can only focus on one.) So you can't focus on the task at hand at the same time as you are evaluating future possibilities or reviewing past learnings. Sorry.

When people believe they're multi-tasking they're actually flitting from one thing to another: 'I am briefly concentrating on what's in front of me, then I stop and compare it with what I performed yesterday, then I think about what might happen if . . .'. That way of thinking is always accompanied by an agitated state of mind. While that doesn't always result in feeling stressed, it is pushing you in that direction. And you will not be operating at peak efficiency.

You may have noticed a macho mentality in some occupations that results in boasts along the lines of, 'It's a tough world out there, and only the tough can cut it'. People saying such things wear their wretchedness as a badge of honour. But if you ask them to identify the working habits of people they admire, they see something very different to their own.

Try it for yourself. Observe the working habits of people you admire – whether they be assistants, middle managers, business leaders – and you will find often they share one characteristic: they have the wherewithal to remain focused on what is before them, no matter what potential distractions surround them. They have the ability to maintain focus or to be mindful in dynamic situations.

For example, some people can grasp the meaning of a document no matter how many others are waiting, or how little time there is before the next meeting. Whether or not they employ a specific methodology such as the one we have been discussing, they certainly have the ability to shift from scattered attention to focused attention very quickly. And to retain that focus longer than most.

This is not just a feature of the workplace. Athletes strive for the ability to be 'in the zone' when they're competing. Artists need a similar singularity of focus to achieve creative depth in their work. So, too, with therapists, coaches and counsellors. It all involves the same approach of directing all of your attention to what is before you. You might wonder, then, why this isn't the default way of approaching all life practices.

There is also a popular line of excuses as to why someone should postpone or avoid doing this. 'I'm a strategic planner; how can I focus on the present when my job requires me to be thinking ahead all the time?' Or, 'I'm a historian; how can I focus on the present when my role is to explore and analyse the past?' Or, 'If I concentrate too much, won't it reduce my ability to relax and enjoy what's going on?' Or, 'If I focus on only one activity, doesn't that prevent me from noticing what's going on in other areas?' Or, 'How can I participate in a conversation at the same time as I'm trying to bring my attention back to the centre?'

Take a slightly less literal view of what 'the present' is, and those concerns disappear. For example, we established earlier that you can either focus on the present, or let your thoughts go wandering off into the past or the future. You understand how that works. But what if your job is planning next year's conference in Hawaii, or working out what your company spent on advertising over the past three years?

Easy. You make it an activity of the present. Every activity can function in this way if you devote all of your attention to it. A task that involves planning or envisioning future scenarios becomes just another activity of the present – if you employ all of your attention. If you ignore distractions. An activity that involves delving into the past becomes an activity of the present – if you do it with all of your attention.

Rather than reducing your capacity for understanding or enjoying what's happening, focusing this way dramatically enhances it.

Try eating an orange slowly and deliberately; you'll be surprised at just how tasty (or sour, or juicy) it is possible for a piece of fruit to be. Does it mean that by eating this way, you won't be aware of other pieces of fruit on your plate? Or other items on the menu? Or other people coming into the cafe? Far from it. You will be as aware of them as you need to be; you just won't be focusing on them.

Next time you're in a conversation, participate with all of your attention. Not analysing your friend's state of mind (though at an intuitive level you may be taking this into account), or planning what you might say next, or working out a response to a veiled criticism, or thinking how attractive her blouse is – but being fully aware of the conversation, the interplay of dialogue and transfer of meaning between one person and another, and the rapport that exists in this special state of attentiveness.

It all comes down to this: if you want to make life richer, more revealing and more satisfying, take to it with all of your attention.

If you want to be more efficient in your work, your art and your sport, take to it with all of your attention.

If you want to go through life with calm and equanimity at your core, take to it with all of your attention.

Here's how to do it in the most effortless and effective way . . .

Inwards

To begin, direct your attention to the physical place you are now. Where your feet touch the floor, or your hands touch the keyboard.

Outwards

Next, direct your attention outwards, in all directions, using your peripheral vision (or hearing).

Inwards

Then, bring your attention back to the task at hand, and keep it focused on that. Do what you're doing to the very best of your abilities.

↔

When the attention wanders, which it will, just redirect it back to the activity. The attention wanders outwards, you bring it back. Simple.

Calm:
no matter what

The moment is here

This book presents five fundamental insights.

The first is that it is possible for you to have an underlying sense of calm and equanimity that sticks with you. You can depend on it, and return to it, no matter what is going on in your life. Good times, bad times, and any moment in between.

The second is that unrest is most likely to occur when your thoughts flit between the future and the past. Conversely, peace of mind, equanimity and contentment exist when your attention rests in the present. You are at your most powerful and efficient when your attention is focused here.

The third is that all of the methods and practices in this book, as well as those you find in most meditation schools, are designed to train the attention to rest in the present. The more you practise this, the more fluid and accessible that ability becomes.

The fourth is that all of the attention-training practices in this book follow the same Outwards→Inwards process, which involves choosing where to direct the attention.

And the final one is that the process itself is what's important, not the results of that process. Enjoy it for what it is, rather than for what it can do for you. Because you will probably never reach the stage where your attention remains permanently in the present. (I've never met anyone who could manage it.) Besides, what would be the point?

There are two versions of the Outwards→Inwards process. Essentially they are the same. The difference is only in application: that they are designed to be used on different occasions. Combined, however, they make up the practice that delivers what this book is about. To recap:

Begin your day with a relaxed, seated practice. The steps are calming and easy to follow. The attention wanders, you bring it back to a central point such as the sound of the out-breath. You do this for 20–30 minutes at a time, on a regular basis. Many would see this as a conventional, concentrative meditation practice.

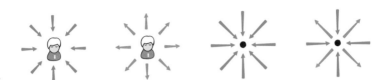

When the Outwards→Inwards process becomes second nature, you can start applying it to everyday life. To the spaces between events (a pause) and to the events themselves.

In the wider application, though, instead of bringing the attention back to the sound of the outbreath as you did in the seated meditation, you bring it back to the activity you're involved in. That may be eating, drinking, working, playing, reading, relaxing, conversing, even enduring a discomfort.

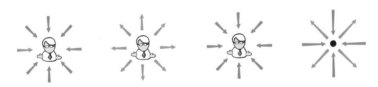

Start out doing this for a few minutes on each occasion, then progressively extend. You may need a reminder in the early days, but eventually it becomes an ingrained approach to life. So much so that in some calm moment in the distant future, you'll look back and wonder what all the fuss was about. Was it ever necessary for you to 'learn' anything?

Practise for a moment

This brings us to the money question: what are you going to do next? What are you going to do to put all this into practice?

What I've presented is a practice so fundamentally simple that it could – *and should* – be basic life training for every child. If you're wondering why it took so many pages to explain, the fact is it didn't. It only required a couple of pages to put across the methodology, the rest of the book has been about convincing you it *is* so simple and down-to-earth.

I have purposely not dwelt on the physiological and emotional benefits that flow from making this a part of your life, other than to say they are cumulative and extend beyond feeling more peaceful and together. The focus of this book has been on the big picture: a lifelong foundation of calm and equanimity.

You are on the way here the instant you stop thinking about what you are doing, or should be doing, and start doing it. That is, applying the Outwards→Inwards process.

From this moment your worldly experience is becoming richer and more fulfilling. Perhaps for the very first time you are sensing what 'at ease' really means. Your capacity to get excited has not changed, you still have mishaps, and you still go through life's usual ups and downs. But at your core is peacefulness and equanimity, and the sense that everything is okay. And although it's hard to express this in more substantial terms, there is growing clarity as well.

The benefits that will be most noticeable are short term ones. The longer term ones creep up on you. We have touched on neuroplasticity, the way the brain changes in accord with changes in your behaviour, circumstances and/or mental practices. You would expect only long-term meditators to enjoy these changes, but recent studies show they may be beginning to take shape after just a few weeks of practice.

The three-in-one approach in this book is designed to accelerate change by effortlessly, and imperceptibly, ramping up the 'practice hours'. You are doing this when you use the Outwards→Inwards process in a structured meditation, and you accelerate the change when you apply it to your everyday activities. You don't have to plan or organise to find suitable opportunities - they are all around you.

So what it boils down to is that you do what you would normally do, only in a more focused fashion. Not continually thinking forwards or backwards as you have always done in the past, but being fully engrossed in the present. *The attention wanders outwards, I direct it back to the activity at hand. Again and again.* You direct all of your attention to the showering, shaving or applying makeup; you don't simultaneously plan the day's activities. You focus on remaining mindful and present on the train trip to work; you don't try to distract yourself with your smartphone. At work, you direct all of your attention to a routine task such as filing, doing it to the best of your ability, appreciating it for the simplicity of what it is, without comparing it to any other activity. At the gym you direct all of your attention to jogging on the treadmill, in contrast to your usual practice of listening to the iPod, watching video hits on the TV, or checking out the physique of the cute trainer. And so it goes throughout the day.

By consciously directing the attention to a few everyday activities – such as those shown in the graphic above – you can effortlessly rack up seven or eight practice hours in a day, without even being aware that you are practising. Just doing what you normally do, but with more intention and focus. One day that unshakeable sense of calm and equanimity will be there. And if you were focused on what you were doing as you were doing it, you wouldn't have even noticed it was happening.

Now I have two more suggestions before I leave you to put this into practice.

BECOME A PRACTITIONER

I've been teaching meditation since the seventies. When I started out I believed all my students were seekers of truth or enlightenment (or whatever it was that seekers were seeking in those days). It turns out that most people who attended my classes and retreats were not like that at all.

In the main, they fell into one of two categories, which I call practitioners and the recreational meditators.

The practitioner meditates regularly, generally on a daily basis. And while they may not be seeking permanent change or improvement, they consider life without their practice would be diminished. They don't consider their practice as something to be analysed, just something to be enjoyed as a seamless part of everyday life. Like their morning cup of tea, the shortcut they take through the park, the unconditional affection of their dog, and the patch of warm sunshine on a cool day.

In contrast to this, the recreational meditator is the one you're most likely to encounter in meditation circles. They represent the major segment of the 'market' and tend to be regulars at talks and retreats. A typical recreational meditator might go to the theatre on occasional Saturdays, play tennis every Sunday, gym every Tuesday and Friday, and fit in a restorative half hour of meditation every few weeks – if they remember, or when they're feeling a touch overwhelmed by something.

Despite their best intentions, meditation is not a central part of the recreational meditator's life. Perhaps as a consequence of this, they compare each meditation sitting with other experiences. 'That was a thoroughly satisfying/ unsatisfying sitting. Better than a massage. I felt uplifted/ transported/blissful/restless/frustrated.' Often they will expect some sort of emotional result to flow from it. 'I've just done half an hour of meditation; I should be feeling different now.' These views have a big influence on how we perceive meditation. It leads us to change from one type of practice to another in the hope of intensifying the experience. It leads us to compare the style and content of different teachers. It determines which teachers prosper and which ones fail.

You have a choice here. You can adopt a practice like a practitioner, or you can pursue occasional emotional experiences like the recreational meditator.

One approach will serve you for the rest of your life, the other is like having a massage or a bowl of spaghetti – maybe satisfying at the time, but hardly important in the grand scheme of things.

I am urging you now – in this very paragraph – to choose to be a practitioner. Forget about trends and individual experiences, forget about finding some previously undisclosed answer or method, and accept that a simple everyday practice such as the one we have covered is the key to fully experiencing the present. It is here where all of the benefits come from.

COMING BACK

Part of the guru game is that somewhere along the track he imparts a 'secret'. An insight, a mantra, *shaktipat* (a kind of instant awakening), or something equally as mysterious. You would be disappointed if I did not have one such secret for you.

Much has been said and written about how to get the most out of meditation. This book says it's all about where you direct your attention, other teachers say other things. Yet in my long experience there is one secret that triumphs.

That secret is coming back to the present.

Just keep coming back. Don't think about what is meant by meditation, don't analyse, don't entertain excuses, and don't make plans. Just start doing it. Turn up, sit down, and direct your attention to the outbreath. Turn up, focus on the activity at hand and direct all of your attention to that. When the attention strays, you direct it back.

Come back to the present, not once a day, not twice, but dozens of times each day. In the morning and/or evening, put aside some sitting time – and don't give another thought to what's meant to happen. When the attention wanders elsewhere, just keep directing it back to the outbreath. You'll